NUCLEAR
P·O·W·E·
The natural radioactivity of coffee beans exceeds the level at which we treat items as low level radioactive waste.
There is nothing wrong with coffee beans. In fact natural radiation occurs in many everyday foodstuffs. It exists in the air, the ground, the buildings around us and even in our radios, TVs and digital watches.
It's really a question of getting radiation into perspective.
To help widen understanding of the key issues of nuclear generated electricity, the British Nuclear Forum have produced a comprehensive information pack.
"I'm no fan of nuclear power."
"I believe nuclear is the power of the future."
"I agree with both of them."
BRITISH NUCLEAR FUELS PLC.
"TO ARREST THE GREENHOUSE EFFECT WE SHOULD CONCENTRATE ON A MASSIVE INCREASE IN NUCLEAR GENERATING CAPACITY"
SCIENTIFICALLY SPEAKING, IT'S JUST A LOT OF HOT AIR.
Nicholas Ridley, the Government, BNFL, and the CEGB claim that nuclear power is an answer to the greenhouse effect.
This view is mistaken.
Moreover, 100 of the country's leading scientists, doctors, and engineers, 40 of whom are listed below, have signed the following declaration:
"NUCLEAR POWER IS NOT AN ANSWER TO THE GREENHOUSE EFFECT.
The nuclear industry is right when it says that the greenhouse effect is a threat to civilisation.
It is wrong when it says that nuclear power has an important part to play in reducing emissions of greenhouse gases.
This is so because the amount of carbon dioxide produced by coal-fired power stations around the world constitutes only a small percentage of the overall greenhouse gases currently added to the atmosphere.
Even a decision to eliminate that small percentage by replacing coal-fired power stations with nuclear stations is a mistake.
This is so because energy efficiency measures offer far more scope than nuclear, £-for-£, in reducing the demand for fossil fuels.
It is cheaper to save a unit of energy than to generate an additional unit.
And the scope for energy efficiency measures is huge in our energy-profligate world economy.
The hundreds of billions of dollars which would have to be spent on an expanded nuclear programme would drain the resources available for energy efficiency and other measures.
Energy efficiency measures can be introduced far more quickly than can nuclear power stations.
Time is not on our side when it comes to tackling the greenhouse effect.
It takes a minimum of six years to build a nuclear power station, and a matter of months to implement energy saving measures.
Finally, the nuclear waste issue is unresolved.
Decommissioning has essentially yet to be addressed.
The problems of nuclear weapons proliferation remain.
And the track record of the nuclear industry involves a long history of over-ambitious appraisals of cost and reactor safety. An expansion of the nuclear programme will compound these problems.
The greenhouse effect is a serious environmental phenomenon which requires serious and urgent solutions.
Nuclear power is irrelevant to the prevention of global warming."
GREENPEACE
LIST OF SIGNATORIES
LET'S CLEAR THE AIR ABOUT COAL.
WAKE UP TO THE NEW AGE OF
British COAL

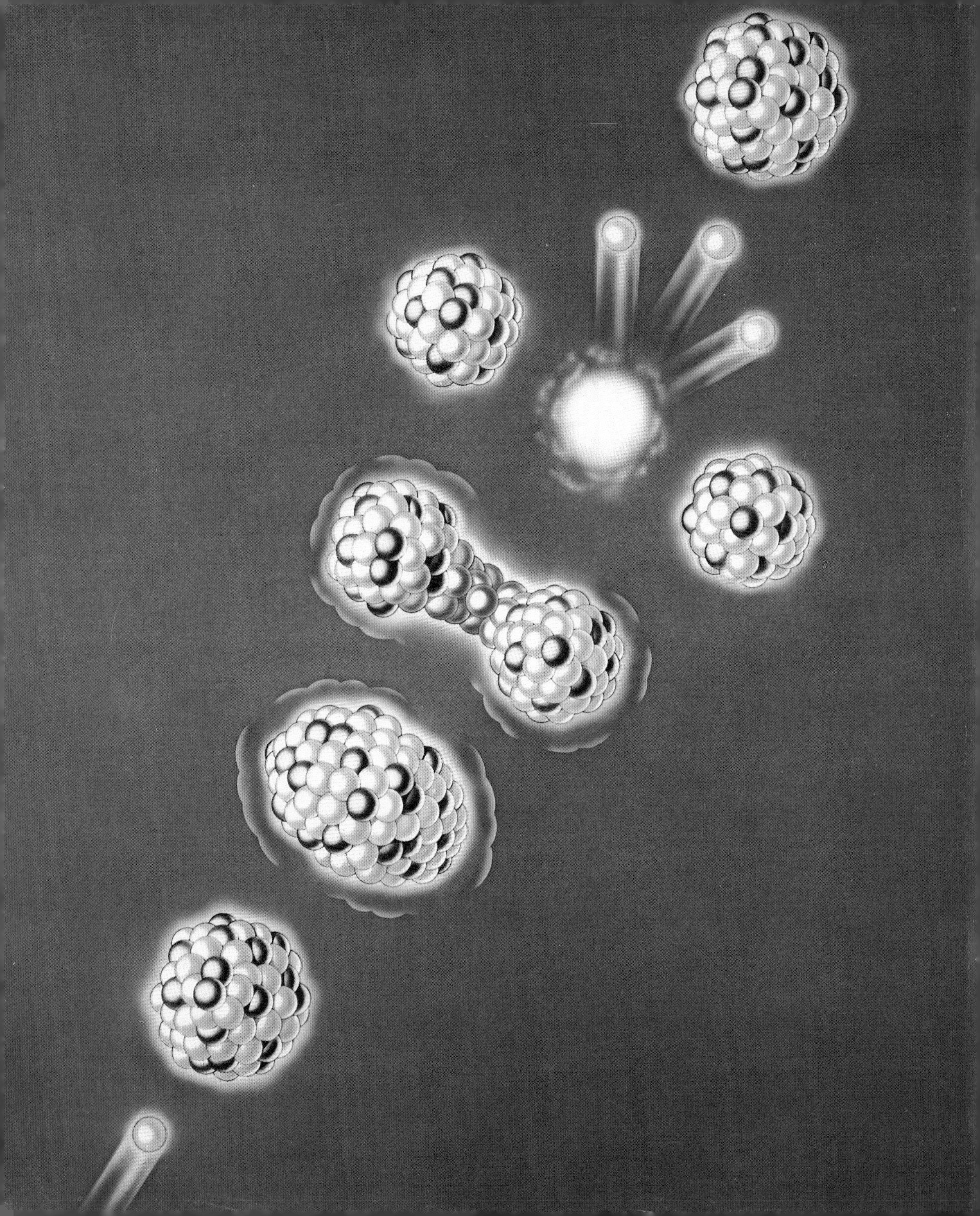

# NUCLEAR P·O·W·E·R

## THE FACTS AND THE DEBATE

PETER KING

QUILLER PRESS
LONDON

# CONTENTS



*Frontispiece:* Diagrammatic representation of nuclear fission: the key to the generation of nuclear power. The nucleus of a uranium atom, when hit by a travelling neutron, splits into two parts, releasing energy in the form of heat. At the same time, several more neutrons are released, and the process continues.


ISBN 1-870948-16-5
First published 1990 by Quiller Press, 46 Lillie Road, London SW6 1TN

The debate about the pros and cons of nuclear power has been active since the 1950s and reached its height in the United Kingdom at the immensely expensive public inquiries mounted for the Sizewell B and Hinkley Point C power stations. Millions of pounds were spent on these inquiries by the government and by the public bodies concerned with the planning applications. In order to participate, organisations like Greenpeace, Friends of the Earth and the Council for the Preservation of Rural England also had to find considerable funds for professional representation.

In general terms it might be said that these 'Green' organisations were opposed to nuclear power, at least in the form in which it was presented as government policy. The media, in the early days of the debate, were polarised. As might be expected, *The Times*, *Daily Telegraph*, *Financial Times* and others followed the government line, while liberal papers like the *Guardian* supported the 'Green' view. Some TV programmes were anti-nuclear, particularly after Chernobyl. Later, the media as a whole began to be sceptical about government policies and even the *Financial Times* and the *Economist* became highly critical.

Of the books that were written in order to present one or other side of the case, the majority were sympathetic to the 'Green' point of view. Many of these presented their views in an extreme form. Those writing to defend nuclear power seemed also to be partial, largely because 'the nationalised structure of the electricity supply industry gave a virtual monopoly of information about nuclear costs to a few people who, in turn, provided governments with the benefit of every doubt to nuclear power. As a result the industry has a history of 30 years of over-optimistic cost forecasts.' I quote from Professor Colin Robinson, Professor of Economics at the University of Sussex.

Other information – in addition to costs – supplied by the industry also tended to be optimistic and it was not until the early 1980s that a more open policy was adopted, largely in response to the increasing volume of criticism in parliament and the media, which by that time was reaching serious proportions. Those members of the public who wished to acquaint themselves with both sides of the debate found it difficult to do so, except by studying parliamentary reports of Select Committees, which dealt with specific aspects of policy. To quote Professor Robinson again, it would be unfortunate if the review of nuclear power policy in the mid-1990s, announced by the government, were once more 'conducted behind closed doors like past nuclear reviews by the Department of Energy, the Atomic Energy Authority and two state nuclear companies.'

In my own attempt to collect information from some interested parties on both sides, it was surprising to be told that nothing could be given me, or that no time could be made available to check the conclusions at which I had arrived. Thus the 'monopoly of information' to which Professor Robinson refers is exacerbated by the refusal of some public and private bodies to contribute information to a debate to which they were such willing contributors (whatever side they were on) when the times suited them. For example, anti-nuclear propaganda declined markedly at the time of the Iraqi crisis in 1990, when the threat to oil supplies became clear to everyone.

That is the background to this book. I hold no firm views on the shape of nuclear power policies for the United Kingdom and am neither 'pro' nor 'anti' in the sense in which these terms are used. I have tried to solicit the views of all those who have had views to express, although I cannot claim that I have read everything on the subject. Nor can I claim to be entirely up to date in a debate which changes with alarming speed as governments make U-turns and what Professor Robinson calls 'the nuclear information monopoly' moves the goal posts.

British Nuclear Fuels plc have taken a special rôle in the genesis of the book in as much as, while its form was my own idea, they have read the text and commented upon it. A copy of the text was also sent to Greenpeace. The involvement of these organisations, however, did not extend to editorial control and the form in which it appears is entirely my own responsibility.

'The best hope for the mid-1990s review is for a degree of openness never seen before in nuclear decision-making. Instead of a White Paper or some other pronouncement handing down decisions already made, a period of debate . . . is required. The debate should start from a neutral base, asking whether there are special features of nuclear power which mean that its development should be either promoted or restrained by the state. When a decision is eventually made, it requires proper explanation, not vague statements that nuclear power is needed on security, environmental or other grounds.' That is Professor Robinson again, and I offer this book as a contribution to the debate.

Peter King
Oxfordshire 1990

# 1. NEED

The equation *civilisation* equals *energy* is a relatively recent way of describing the development of human kind. In older times *civilisation* equalled *religion* and, later, *mechanisation, transportation* or *education.* Today, it is energy which, in the words of the song, 'makes the world go round'.

A recent report by the Trades Union Congress described how energy is fundamental to most of the things we use, the places where we work, the transport we employ, even our health and well-being. The harnessing of energy sources for human ends includes 'water power, windmills, beasts of burden, firewood, coal, steam, oil and petrol, coal gas and natural gas, peat, nuclear power, solar power, tidal power, refuse incineration and heat from below the earth's surface'. Some of these forms of energy we take so much for granted that they become virtually invisible. For example we see the sun, but do not think of its rays as potential energy. The same with the waves of the sea. Even the electricity which comes to us by the simple flick of a switch is, in a sense, invisible energy because we do not know whether its source was a coal-fired power station, an oil-fired station or a nuclear-powered station. If we live in the North of Scotland, there is a good chance that it might have been energy from a hydro-electric scheme, but as a user or consumer we would still probably be unaware of the source of the light or heat it generates.

Thus the *source* of the energy is irrelevant to most users, but some understanding of the various sources available is essential to an appreciation of the newest, nuclear power.

The most common fuels used to produce energy in Britain and the developed world are the so-called fossil fuels. These are coal ('hard' coal, and 'brown' coal), oil, natural gas and peat. For the past 200 years these have been the basis of the growth of what we call 'our' world. It was not always so. Primitive man would have used firewood for cooking his food and keeping warm, and an individual's total consumption of energy in prehistoric times has been calculated at 10-12,000 kilocalories a day. By the Middle Ages, average energy consumption per individual had doubled, mainly through the extra demand for heat to smelt metals and forge iron. Today, the average individual's energy consumption in our affluent society is fifty times greater than our neolithic forebears. A high-spending, Porsche-owning, jet-setting citizen probably uses two or three times the average.

Most people would agree with the Atomic Energy Authority's view that:

> Energy provides the power to progress. With a sufficiency of energy properly applied a people can rise from subsistence level to the highest standard of living. From this it seems to follow that the more energy is available, and the more it can be 'properly applied', the more it will be possible to 'progress' from subsistence levels to higher standards of living, not only in the developed countries but in the Third World.

But not everyone sees it like that. The Greens, for example, argue that 'more' does not always lead to 'progress'. They ask:

> If we in Britain have already reached sufficiency in energy supply, why is our society increasingly impoverished? And how is it that in Africa, where there has been a steady growth in energy use over the past few decades, more misery and starvation exists than ever before?

Others, like Dr Schumacher, argue that small is beautiful and the answer to third world under-development is appropriate technology, not increased supplies of energy.

This point of view, whatever its merits, cannot alter the fact that energy is more and more in demand, and to produce that energy we cannot continue to rely on the fossil fuels as if they were endless. They are not. The Green supporters, when asked whether we could run out of energy, roundly answer:

> No. As energy sources become scarcer, prices will rise and consumption will fall, as happened following the 1973 Arab oil embargo. We still have considerable reserves of fossil fuels: at present rates of consumption, enough commercially exploitable oil to last 100 years. Proved reserves of natural gas are 50 billion barrels (enough for 50 years at current annual consumption), with remaining undiscovered reserves estimated at more than three times that. Unconventional sources could conceivably double the production again. Therefore natural gas supplies should be available for another century at least. World coal resources are estimated at more than 10,000 billion tonnes, exploitable reserves are put at a much lower figure of 640 billion tonnes, giving some 250 years of production at current rates.

This analysis paints a reassuring picture but it is far from being universally accepted. For example Sir Brian Flowers, in his 1976 Report, believed that the extent of oil reserves was 80 years at current consumption but, if this continued to increase, 'reserves will last only

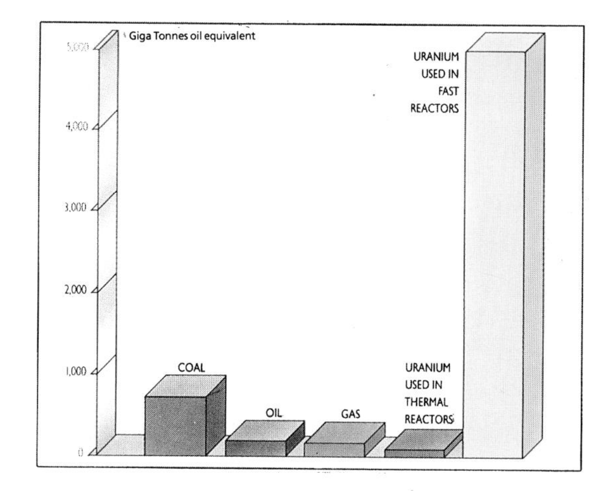


Fossil fuels – coal, oil and gas – will not last for ever. The uranium presently used in nuclear reactors is also limited in quantity – perhaps enough to last 50 years – because any more would be too costly to recover. However the next generation of reactors, the so-called 'fast' reactor, can use uranium discarded as waste by present-day stations.

until about the year 2000.' Since annual consumption of natural gas was then less than half that of oil, reserves of it would last over 150 years, or until the year 2010 if the present increase in consumption continued. Coal, thought Flowers, might last out for another 200 years, or not so long if oil and gas ran out and more coal was needed. A more recent analysis (BP Statistical Review of World Energy, 1987) allows for 30 more years of oil and 60 years of gas reserves at present rates of consumption. New resources are still being discovered.

Oil is one of the most widely used sources of energy, although today British oil-fired power stations supply only about one sixth as much electricity to the grid as that provided by the nuclear stations. Everyone assumes that oil will progressively fade from the scene as a source of electric power. This is partly because it is popularly believed that little remains to be discovered; some oil experts, however, believe that further discoveries could be made in the North Sea and elsewhere. Another argument is

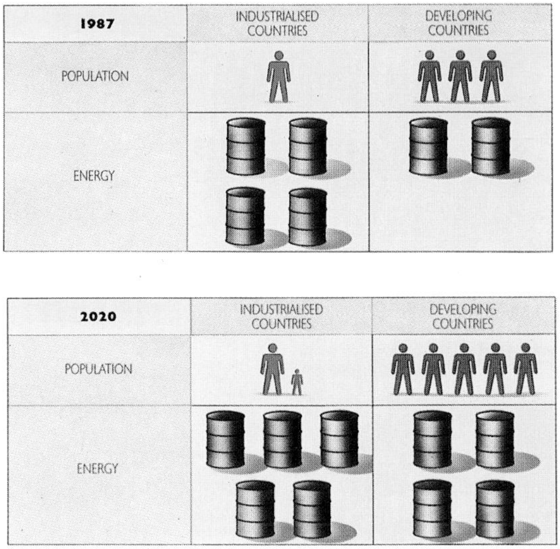

| 1987 | INDUSTRIALISED COUNTRIES | DEVELOPING COUNTRIES |
|---|---|---|
| POPULATION | | |
| ENERGY | | |

| 2020 | INDUSTRIALISED COUNTRIES | DEVELOPING COUNTRIES |
|---|---|---|
| POPULATION | | |
| ENERGY | | |

Growth in population and energy demand 1987-2020. This shows in diagramatic form how the world's energy demands are growing while the developing world's population expands.

that oil is better utilised for other purposes – for example, as a feed stock for the chemical and plastics industries.

A more pressing reason why the planners discount oil is worries about the wild fluctuations in its price. From an era of very cheap supplies, at around $2 a barrel, the crises of 1973-4 and 1979-81 drove the price up to some $40 a barrel, through the actions of the OPEC cartel. Eight years later, some members of the same cartel indulged in overproduction, and the price fell to about $20. If it continued to fall, the effect on US producers and on existing North Sea oil fields might be that they could no longer afford to produce. Another reason for the drop in oil prices was the increasing substitution of nuclear power, which effectively replaced billions of barrels of oil each year over the past decade. When demand falls, prices fall too.

With the world's largest reserves held in the Middle East, no government outside that area wishes to depend again on an energy source which may rocket in price so dramatically as oil. This was the major reason for the French switch to nuclear dependency and is at the root of the British government's determination to diversify away from oil towards nuclear power – just as it wants to diversify away from coal because of union-controlled fluctuations in supply. Another factor against British reliance on oil is the geographical location of the major sources in the Middle East. In the summer of 1990, the Kuwait/Iraq crisis resulted in an immediate price rise.

Those whose function is to supply and sell electricity argue that all fossil fuels may run out comparatively quickly. They point out that, for the chemical industry, both oil and natural gas will have to be replaced by coal and this will make it increasingly difficult to obtain adequate supplies for the power stations.

The Trades Union Congress has voted in favour of greater reliance on coal and notes that there are major disagreements between experts about the extent of fossil fuel reserves, varying from between 30 and 100 years' supply of oil, more for gas, rather less for peat. Yet they admit that fossil fuel supplies are limited. 'Some time in the next hundred years, perhaps in the next ten years, they will start to become scarce again and rise rapidly in price, causing new energy crises if we are not prepared,' they say.

The simple fact is that the fossil fuels, the product of trees and vegetation squashed for millions of years between layers of rock and soil, may one day be exhausted, with no possibility of finding any more or making any more. The inevitable conclusion seems to be that we must use our remaining supplies of fossil fuel more efficiently, so that they last longer, and we must also find alternatives.

The Greens put much more emphasis on conservation. They claim that 'there is no simple relationship between energy consumption per capita and quality of life, nor between energy consumption and gross national product, or economic activity generally.' We could therefore live a good life on a much lower consumption of energy – and world reserves will last longer. More efficient use of resources is also necessary to deal with an expanding population, with 80 to 90 per cent of the world's citizens in the developing countries. Again, world population is expected to double in the next 50 years and double again in the following 50. Conservation alone will not compensate fully for this.

The Greens' argument focuses on the comparative inefficiency of electricity as a form of energy. The Flowers Report suggested that while electricity accounts for about one third of all primary energy used in the UK, it provides only about one eighth of that used by end consumers. 'It is inherently wasteful to use electricity as a source of heat', claimed Flowers. The overall efficiency of the most efficient power station is 37 per cent, while the overall efficiency for the UK electricity industry was 27 per cent, Flowers calculated. (The operators say that there has been an improvement since his report.)

Major Uses of Electricity in England and Wales 1987/88

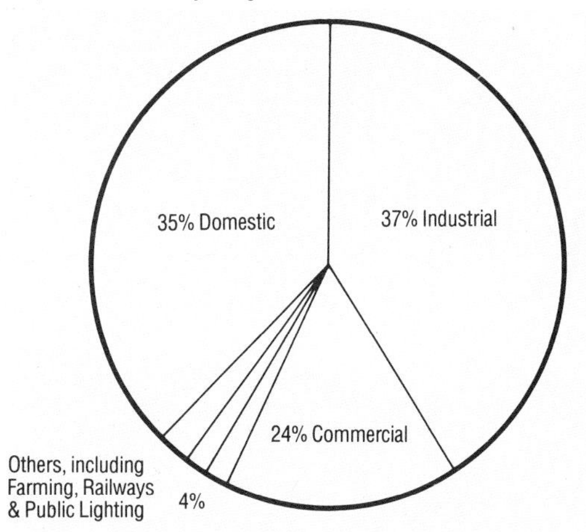


The Greens claim that electricity is an inherently wasteful form of energy because approximately two-thirds of the power produced by UK power stations is not used by the consumer. They advocate alternatives for city dwellers, such as CHPs which use household rubbish, amongst other fuels.

The Greens support the view that new types of plant should be introduced to generate electricity much more efficiently. As examples they cite central, or district, heating schemes from CHPs (combined heat and power plants), which burn a variety of fuels including household rubbish. They point out that Holland already has 600 small plants of this kind and the USA plans to install thousands.

By contrast the supply industry forecasts that UK demand for electricity will actually increase over coming years, as it has over the past five years. Even with consumers becoming more energy efficient, it believes that demand for electricity will grow at a rate of between one and two per cent until the turn of

Million tonnes of oil equivalent saved by use of nuclear power.

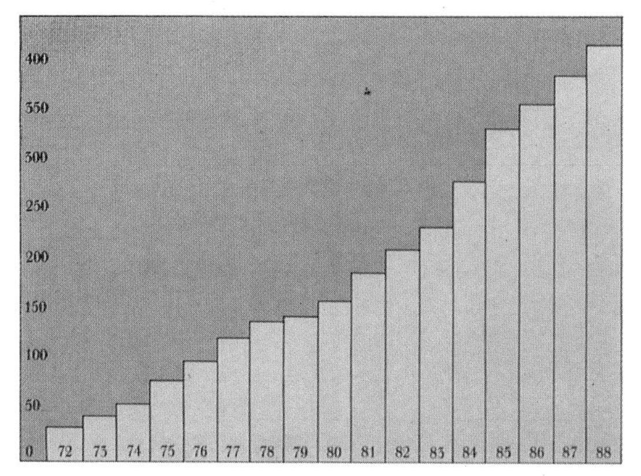


One reason for the fluctuations in the price of oil has been that the worldwide use of nuclear power now replaces the burning of over 400 million tonnes of oil, or over 600 million tonnes of coal, each year.

the century. In a free society, this growing demand will have to be met, unless it is argued that such a demand is anti-social. Demand increases for a mixture of reasons, including the changing requirements of commerce and industry (which take 60 per cent of the electricity supply), changes in transport policy, in pricing and in advertising which persuades the consumer to change to electricity – and a vast range of others. To control all these factors would be extremely difficult in a market economy.

It is not only the increased demand for electricity that creates a need for new power stations, but also the fact that older power stations are reaching the end of their useful lives and have to be replaced. So the question of what type of fuel is to be used to produce electricity is one which must be answered now. In fact, the Department of Energy and the supply industry are already making a considerable investment in possible alternatives, particularly wind and water.

The supply industry is in no doubt that future energy requirements exceed their foreseeable ability to supply electricity. If they are right, then regardless of the time-span over which fossil fuels remain available, new capacity must be set up to fill the forecast gap, and the decision about what type of fuel will be burnt in these new stations is a critical one.

Such forecasts of a gap should perhaps be regarded with some caution. The view that there will be a demand for more power than will be available is based both on forecasts of demand and on estimates of available supply; in the event, the so-called 'capacity shortfall' might well be reduced by what the industry call 'sensitivities' affecting available supply. For example, it would be possible to extend the useful life of each of the bigger coal-fired stations to 45 years, instead of closing them down after 40 years as planned. This would increase capacity, but there would be attendant disadvantages, just as there are when we hang on to an old car instead of trading it in for a new one. Even taking such 'sensitivities' into account, the supply industry estimates that with demand growing to the year 2000 at

To generate the same amount of electricity as a modern nuclear power station produces would need:

Wind – 300 60 metre diameter wind turbines covering an area about the size of Birmingham

Solar – 150 square kilometres of solar panels

Wave – 100 kilometres of wave energy converters

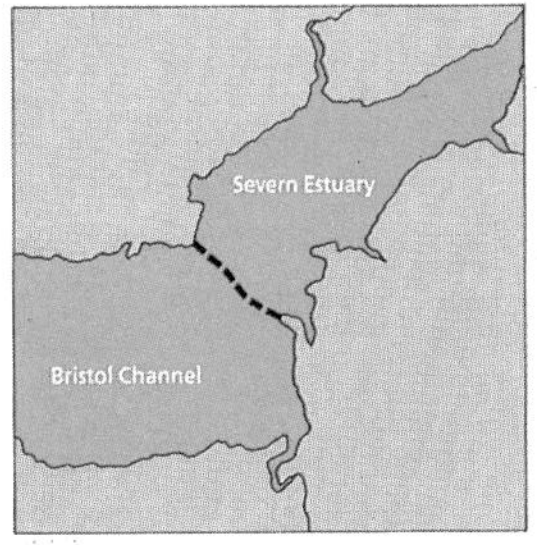


Tidal – A tidal barrier across the Severn Estuary about 10 miles long might generate the same amount of electricity as 1½ nuclear power stations

Hydro – A hydro station about 10 times the size of the largest station in Britain (130 MW).

Alternative energy sources should be substituted for inefficient electricity generation, according to the Greens. But the energy supply industry believes that relatively few of these alternatives are viable, and those that are would introduce their own environmental problems.

between one and two per cent per annum, the gap will still be there.

The question for the UK supply industry therefore is how to meet this gap, or, at any rate, reduce it. Originally, a major element in its plans was the construction of new nuclear power stations of the PWR type at Sizewell, Hinkley Point and at two other sites, but this was radically modified by a change in government policy in late 1989. Coal-fired stations will be needed too, and other 'conventional' options such as combined cycle gas turbines are currently being planned.

In 1985, when selecting more nuclear power plant to meet the forecast need for electricity, and so close the foreseen demand/supply gap, the CEGB based part of its case for building the Sizewell station on the supposed shortage of fossil fuels. Three years later, however, when putting its case for the second PWR station at Hinkley, the Board did not pursue this point (perhaps they felt it could be taken for granted) and instead relied on the need for 'diversity'.

The need for diversity in energy sources, under discussion for some years, was given the imprimatur of authority by the Conservative Party in 1979, when it was enshrined in their election manifesto. Diversity in this case meant, in effect, that a significant proportion of energy generation must in future be from non-fossil sources.

When the Conservative government came to power that year it took steps to put its manifesto promise into effect. The long and protracted Sizewell inquiry of 1983-5 was part of this process. Once approval had been given to build a new PWR station at Sizewell, the government continued to insist that more nuclear power should be an integral part of national energy policies. Answering a question in the House of Commons in December 1987,

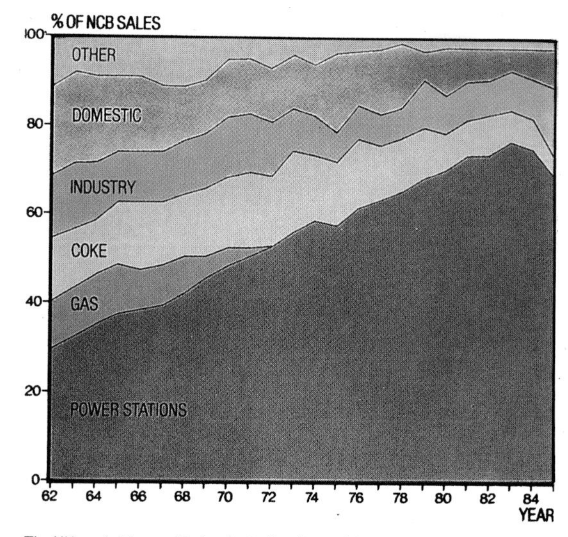


The UK market for coal is dominated by demand from power stations. Government policy is to diversify away from coal. The dip in 1984 reflects the miners' strike.

the then Secretary of State for Energy, Cecil Parkinson, said 'We cannot afford to risk dependency on one source of power alone (coal). There is an obvious need for diversity.' And when, two months later, he introduced his White Paper on privatisation of the electricity industry, he added: 'We believe it is in the national interest to have diversity – and nuclear power is part of that diversity. . . . It has been a declared policy of the Government.'

In fact, although the Secretary of State did not say so, the diversity policy was based not only on a fear that fossil fuels were finite but also on a desire to avoid over-dependence on coal mined by the National Union of Mineworkers. Two bitter confrontations between this union and Conservative governments had resulted in a resolve never again to rely too heavily on a single source of energy if it were possible to have an alternative. And whatever their political affiliations, the British public at large probably support the Conservative view. Another factor influencing the government was of course the oil price crisis of 1973-4 and 1979-80. Oil was down to $20 a barrel by 1989, but fear of an Arab monopoly remained one sound reason for going nuclear.

This policy of diversification away from coal and oil was further enshrined in legislation formulated in the 1988 White Paper on electricity privatisation, which proposed that the new commercial electricity-distributing companies would be under a statutory duty to contract for a minimum of non-fossil-fuelled generation. This minimum had to be not less than the present level of existing and committed nuclear and renewable (i.e. other non-fossil fuel) generating capacity, and would probably be about 20 per cent of total capacity. So the supply industry, in putting its proposals forward for more nuclear stations, had to prove that nuclear stations were more satisfactory than other types of non-fossil source. We shall consider the latter in a moment.

In requesting permission to build more PWR-type nuclear stations, the industry might also have been expected to show that this particular type was more satisfactory than other types of nuclear station, notably the second-generation AGR type, but they could claim that this debate had been won at the Sizewell inquiry, when the Inspector in charge had expressed himself satisfied that the PWR was the better design. Not all the evidence supported this view.

At any rate, the case for building more PWR power stations of the Sizewell type rested on the conviction that existing power stations had to be replaced and a prospective shortfall in supply had to met, and that government policy clearly required that further coal and fossil-fuelled stations must be complemented by non-fossil types.

The remaining task was to prove to general satisfaction that the nuclear solution was preferable to the other available non-fossil alternatives.

Many books have been written on each of these alternative energy sources, proving that one or another offers the solution to the world's (or the nation's) energy requirements. Interest in some of them, like the possibility of harnessing tidal power, goes back for centuries. And there are experts who believe that not enough research has ever been devoted to studying such alternatives. This

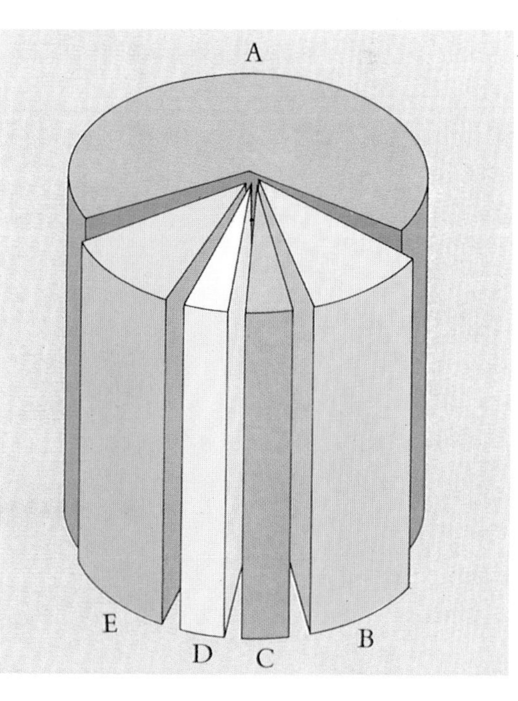


CEGB research expenditure (1987/88) was overwhelmingly in support of nuclear, rather than renewable energy

[A] Nuclear generation 74%
[B] Environment 11%
[C] Transmission and system control 3%
[D] Renewable energy sources 2%
[E] Conventional generation 10%

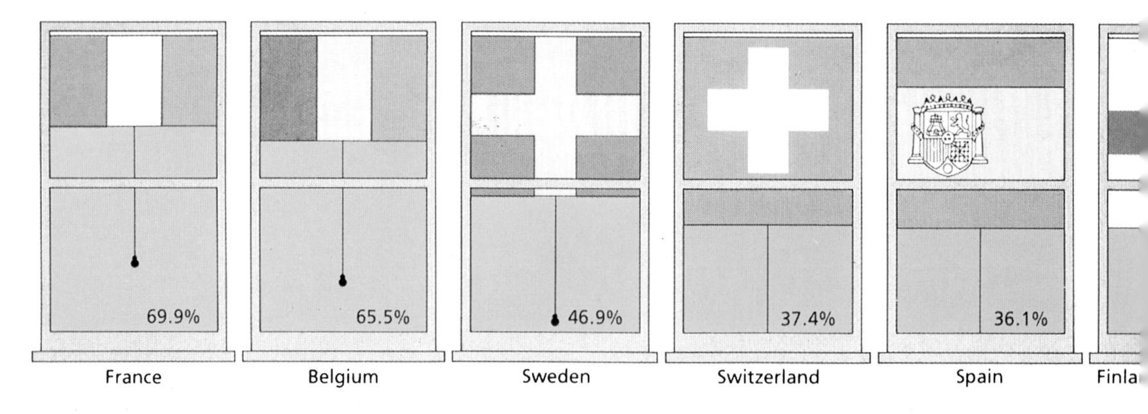


Britain is relatively low in the league of nuclear power users. This 'window' chart shows that in 1988 the proportion of total electricity generated that was supplied by nuclear power was under 20 per cent in the UK, compared to nearly 70 per cent in France. Some of the French 'nuclear' electricity, however, will shortly be exported to the British grid.

apathy has perhaps arisen from the government's conviction that alternative fuels had little to offer. For example, in their oral evidence to the 1976 Flowers Commission, officials from the Department of Energy said that alternative sources, even if successfully developed, could make only 'a marginal contribution' to national needs. Very small sums were allocated to research into alternatives, as against the vast amounts invested in the nuclear option – £14 million annually as against £225 million annually, in 1986.

Exponents of the various alternatives, and those who, like the Greens, do not prefer the nuclear solution, assert that it is because of the inadequacy of research funds that the supply industry has concluded that alternatives cannot meet its future needs. Put money behind them, say the critics, and alternatives would be proved viable. Greenpeace calculates that nuclear power has cost the British taxpayer and electricity consumer about £7 billion (at current prices) in research and development.

Most of these alternatives are described as 'renewable', meaning that, unlike the fossil-based fuels, there is no apparent risk of their running out. Those considered as possible

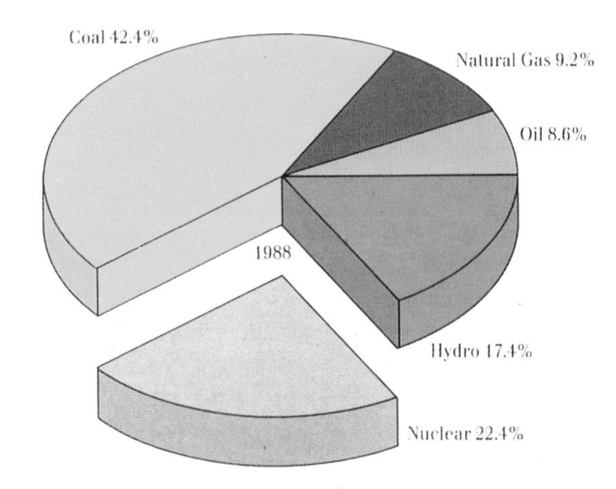


Nuclear power now provides more than one fifth of the electricity in OECD countries, although the figure is boosted by the very high percentage in France and Germany.

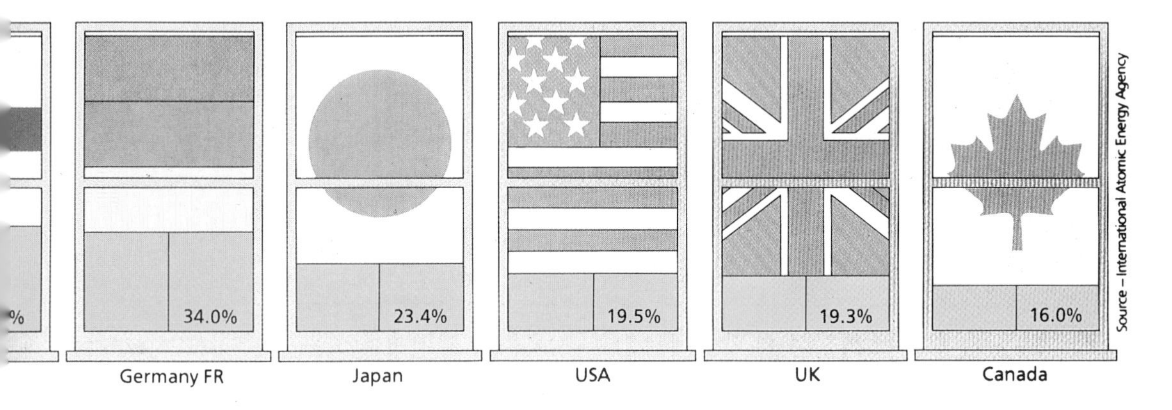


alternatives to nuclear power are wind, tidal, refuse, solar, geothermal and wave power. (Hydro-electric power is now already well developed, but future sites are limited.) Within the scope of this book it is impossible to give a reasoned discussion of all their advantages and disadvantages, and what follows is a summary of the points made for each of them in the CEGB's Statement of Case at Hinkley.

The CEGB has had experience of land-based wind turbines (offshore wind turbines have not yet been developed) at Carmarthen Bay and in the Orkneys; a larger machine is under construction in Kent. The Department of Energy and the CEGB have proposals for three 'wind farms' in Cornwall, West Wales and the northern Pennines. These are far removed from the conventional windmill which pipes water or mills grain. Each wind turbine is a high-tech device as tall as Nelson's Column, with rotors 30 metres across. Each wind farm would contain 25 wind turbines, cover some four square kilometres and generate 8 MW of electricity.

To produce the same amount of electricity as a big nuclear station like Hinkley, there would have to be about 3000 mills of this type, covering an area of about 500 square kilometres. This would be about the size of the Birmingham conurbation, assuming they could be regularly spaced. More widely-spaced, bigger wind generators would produce more power, but none has yet been fully tested. Experience in California has been that the actual performance of a large number of windmills is most disappointing, owing to the unreliability of the machinery.

Based on the costs of the three proposed wind parks, the UK supply industry says wind turbines could produce electricity at a comparable cost to Hinkley and could be in service by the year 2005 at the earliest, but would produce only relatively small output. They sum up land-based wind technology as 'promising but uncertain'.

The development of tidal generation in Britain is at present concentrated on the proposed Severn Barrage, research into which began in 1978. It could be completed early next century. A smaller scheme is also envisaged for the Mersey, which could be developed more quickly.

These two tidal schemes are said to have unfavourable costs compared with the nuclear PWR. There would also be environmental considerations – as there would for the wind option – which have led some Green organisations to oppose tidal schemes. Taking these into account, the CEGB suggested that the schemes would be unlikely to be pursued unless there were benefits additional to electricity generation, such as a road across the barrier or leisure activities. In any event, no other major tidal scheme apart from the Severn is likely to be viable in the UK.

Dealing with the subject of generating electricity by burning household and industrial refuse, the CEGB seemed to agree that this could be used in large cities, partly for process or space heating, because it is a 'proven technology'. However the Board pointed out that there are only four plants currently in operation in the UK; another 10 to 20 would be needed to provide 200 MW of capacity within a reasonable time limit. Since Hinkley's output was planned to be 1000 MW, the CEGB argued that refuse is not a viable alternative to nuclear power.

Hydro-electric (water) power is a proven method of generating electricity, both for the north of Scotland and via the grid to the south of England. The oldest plant at Cwm Dyli, Wales, is 80 years old and its capacity, although quite small, is now being doubled. But, according to the CEGB, only 'small scale opportunities remain in the United Kingdom... the total resource is no more that a few hundred megawatts of which 50 MW appear to be exploitable in the short term.' There are also environmental objections to the spread of hydro-electric schemes.

Solar energy was dismissed by the CEGB as of no interest for large-scale electricity generation in the foreseeable future 'because of the relatively low level of solar radiation here and the high cost of photovoltaic energy converters. . . . It would require a major technological breakthrough in semiconductor technology for photovoltaics to become of value.'

Underground deposits of hot water in porous rocks can provide geothermal energy, as they commonly do in New Zealand. But the UK Department of Energy, which researched the subject between 1976 and 1986, concluded that 'there is little prospect of their being exploited economically here.' The Department is still funding a research programme on hot dry rocks which started in 1976 in Cornwall, but this particular energy source has never been used for electricity generation: the CEGB, while calling it 'promising', has said it is unlikely to be available until into the next century.

Finally, after ten years' research into what was regarded as one of the most attractive of renewable energy technologies, the Department of Energy concluded that large, offshore wave power devices were unlikely to be economical in the United Kingdom in the foreseeable future and has suspended its research. Some work is continuing on small in-shore wave power devices, the CEGB reported.

In sum, therefore, the CEGB's study of renewable energy suggested that the only sources with the potential to contribute capacity on a substantial scale by the year 2000 are tidal and wind power. Refuse, while potentially economic, is limited in scale. Both tidal and wind were, according to the CEGB, less economically attractive than nuclear power.

Critics of the supply industry and of the Government's nuclear plans contest this view. As already noted, they believe renewable research has been starved of funds. They claim that the Department of Energy has estimated that the total contribution of renewable sources to Britain's needs could be the equivalent of two million tonnes of coal by the year 2000.

The critics suggest that renewables could

British nuclear power stations and manufacturing facilities.

supply half the nation's needs by the year 2025, even assuming no new technological breakthroughs. The Greens point out that Denmark installed 400 small wind turbines in 1984 and now has 1400 linked to the system. France has been installing geothermal schemes at the rate of twenty or so per year. They call for Britain to do likewise, and in addition to build small refuse-burning CHP plants and to use tidal energy, more hydro-electricity and wave power schemes. Privatisation of the electricity industry, however, makes investment in research into these renewables less rather than more likely.

Equally important to the debate about sources of energy is the discussion about the ways in which we use energy.

> The majority of energy required in an industrial economy is not high-grade or high-temperature energy like electricity, but low-grade heat. . . . There are untold opportunities to improve the efficiency with which we use all the various kinds of energy. Unglamorous technologies like thermal insulation, heat pumps, and the combined generation of heat and electricity can increase spectacularly the amount of use we get from every unit of energy converted.

So says the TUC.

This may be true, but the great debate on the need for nuclear power still holds the centre of attention. Is it safe, is it economic, is it inseparable from military security? These were the questions which began to be asked back in the 1950s when the Government was worried about how to fill the foreseen energy gap. More recently, according to the electricity supply industry, 'long-term estimates of supply and demand for fossil fuels look in better balance' and the emphasis has shifted to nuclear power as an 'alternative' source of supply rather than a replacement.

A major statement of Government policy on nuclear power made in November 1989 by John Wakeham, Secretary of State for Energy, announced a slow-down in the programme for new nuclear stations, yet stressed that 'We want to preserve the strategic role of nuclear power in order to maintain adequate diversity of electricity supply, to avoid too great a reliance on a single fuel, and obtain the benefits of this environmentally clean source of energy.' The Minister concluded that the government wished to maintain the nuclear option. One way in which this was done was by continuing the construction of the Sizewell B PWR power station and keeping the Magnox reactors in service. A report by the Health and Safety Executive's Nuclear Installation Inspectorate in mid-1990 concluded that the reactors at Calder Hall in Cumbria and Chapelcross in Dumfriesshire, which started operations 30 years ago, would be safe to continue in service for a further decade, subject to certain conditions.

Today, major emphasis is placed by the industry on the fact that nuclear power is kinder to the environment because 'it neither contributes to the greenhouse effect nor produces acid rain; burning coal does both.' These issues will be discussed in later chapters, but before doing so it will be useful to put the debate in perspective by briefly considering the background to the development of nuclear energy over the last hundred years.

# 2. A CENTURY OF DEVELOPMENT

The Victorian sage Samuel Butler wrote: 'Every man's work . . . is always a portrait of himself.' While it would be fascinating to be able to describe the nuclear power 'works' of the second half of the twentieth century in terms of the men responsible for them, it is too early yet to write a history of nuclear power in terms of its personalities. But some names and dates provide a key to its earliest origins.

*1896* Henri Becquerel discovered the phenomenon of radioactivity, but a year later realised its ill-effects when a piece of radium he was carrying in his pocket burnt through to his skin.

*1900s* Great names like Rutherford, Bohr, Summerfield, Einstein, Moseley and Blackett were involved in the study of the atomic nucleus.

*1914* H. G. Wells the novelist published *The World Set Free,* forecasting the release of nuclear energy and the outbreak of nuclear war.

*1930* The Joliot-Curie Institute in Paris unknowingly created the world's first portable neutron source and published their discovery two years later. Their emphasis was not on the neutron to trigger a bomb, but on a 'boiler' setting up a nuclear chain reaction which could be used for nuclear power.

*1932* Chadwick discovered the neutron. In the same year John Cockcroft and Ernest Walton, working under a New Zealander, Professor Ernest Rutherford, split the atom at the Cavendish Laboratory, Cambridge.

*1938-9* Three discoveries that held the key to the practical application of nuclear physics were made within six months of each other and published internationally by Hahn and Strassmann (Berlin), Halbamn, Joliot-Curie and Kowanski (Paris) and Bohr and Wheeler (Copenhagen).

This skeletal history shows the international nature of the work up to the outbreak of World War II. During the course of that war, the British desperately tried to maintain a position in the fission club, despite meagre resources. Churchill came to the conclusion that the British had no alternative but to accept a minor role in a joint bomb project with the United States and Canada. The US project was code-named Manhattan.

*December 1942* Enrico Fermi, a refugee from Rome, and his team started up the world's first 'nuclear reactor' in a disused squash court beneath the football stadium at the University of Chicago. This demonstrated the principle of fission, and also showed that uranium could be turned into plutonium, in whatever quantity desired; every reactor burning uranium since then has done the same. A series of enormous reactors was built along the Columbia river, in the state of Washington, to produce plutonium for the wartime Manhattan bomb project.

*6 August 1945* An atomic bomb was dropped on Hiroshima, Japan, and three days later a second bomb on Nagasaki.

*7 November 1945* Winston Churchill told

Henri Becquerel

Lord Rutherford

Alfred Einstein

Niels Bohr

the House of Commons: 'This I take it is already agreed; we should make atomic bombs.' In order to do so, Britain had to make its own plutonium, because immediately after the end of the war the US Congress passed an Act, named after the American senator Robert McMahon, which denied the British access to America's nuclear developments. A desire to secure military independence has been at the heart of British nuclear policy ever since. And for many years, the military need to a large extent dictated the structure of the nuclear power industry.

*1946* The Labour Cabinet under Clement Atlee took the formal decision to build British bombs – something like 200 were required. Professor John Cockcroft became the Director of Atomic Research and set up office on a site at Harwell, Oxfordshire. The headquarters of a production division was set up under Christopher Hinton at Risley in Cheshire; and factories were established at Springfields, Lancashire, for uranium fabrication, at Windscale, Cumbria, for plutonium extraction, and at Capenhurst in Cheshire for uranium enrichment. The uranium had to be imported and then enriched by artificially increasing the proportion of U235. A weapons establishment was set up, later centred at Aldermaston in Berkshire. Prime Minister Atlee saw to it that all this work had top priority, despite the country's economic weakness, although Christopher Hinton himself wanted waste heat from the plutonium production piles at Windscale to be used to generate electricity. The first bars of uranium were cast from ore at Springfields in 1948 and the two reactors had begun to produce plutonium by 1951.

*1952* Britain's first bomb was tested in the Pacific off the north-west coast of Australia.

*1953* President Eisenhower announced the Atoms for Peace programme. This was intended to preserve US domination in the nuclear field and prevent proliferation of weapon development. A Conservative government under Winston Churchill had come to power in 1951 and co-operation with the Americans had improved. Hitherto, emphasis had been on the military programme, but now Duncan Sandys, Minister of Supply (a Ministry dealing with both military and civil projects), produced his White Paper, *A Programme of Nuclear Power,* which proposed developing a fast breeder reactor (FBR) and building a nuclear power station. The latter was to be Calder Hall near Windscale.

*1954* The USS *Nautilus* submarine was

Enrico Fermi

H.G. Wells

Sir John Cockcroft

Sir Christopher Hinton

launched. The US Navy had developed a nuclear plant for submarines because, unlike oil-fuelled engines, these do not use oxygen for combustion and can stay submerged longer. The fuel elements were immersed in ordinary water – a Pressurised Water Reactor (PWR). By 1957, a similar type of unit was working on shore at a power station near Philadelphia. The PWR went on to become the world's most popular type of design for power stations in the 1960s and beyond.

*1954* The UK Atomic Energy Authority was set up under Sir Edwin Plowden. This had responsibility both for the British bomb and the design of the nuclear power programme, with the main emphasis on the Calder Hall type of station. Cockcroft remained in charge of research and Hinton of the industrial group.

*1955* The Minister of Fuel and Power announced a Ten Year Plan for UK nuclear stations of the Calder Hall type. More reactors were to be built at Calder Hall, and two almost identical ones at Chapelcross, Dumfriesshire, Scotland, a total of eight in all, four reactors at each. These stations were called the Magnox type because the fuel was clad in a special alloy called Magnox.

*1956* Queen Elizabeth II switched power from Calder Hall into the National Grid. This was believed at the time to be a 'British first', but the fact is now established that the then-secret Soviet reactor at Obninsk was giving an output of 5 MW two years earlier.

Critics of the British programme point out that nuclear power would not have been developed so early in Britain, if at all, without the military's requirements: the latter's need for plutonium resulted in a compromise design

In the mid 1950s the US-built *Nautilus*, the world's first nuclear-powered submarine, was launched. Its power plant had to be water-cooled because of the need for prolonged underwater operation and this proved to be a highly practical design which was readily convertible to use for land-based stations. Many have been exported and the newest British type is of this Pressurised Water (PWR) design.

Sir Winston Churchill

Clement Attlee

President Eisenhower

Lord Plowden

for the power stations, which were gas-cooled and graphite-moderated. The US designs, however, much more commercially successful than the British, also had their origin in the nuclear requirements of their armed services.

*1956* The AEA reviewed its reactor design programme. One of its decisions was to abandon the pressurised water reactor (PWR), against the advice of private industry. As noted above, the PWR was in fact to prove the most successful of commercial reactors, first in the USA, then elsewhere, so Britain was left behind, concentrating on less successful types.

The Suez war had aroused fears that Middle East oil supplies would no longer flow to the UK, so when Harold Macmillan became Prime Minister after Suez and took direct responsibility for the AEA, he authorised an increase in the nuclear building programme to 6000 MW by 1965. Hinton, convinced that oil and coal supplies would not decline in the long run, despite the problems of Suez and the higher cost of oil which resulted, cut the programme. More nuclear stations of the Magnox type were ordered at Bradwell in Essex, Berkeley in Gloucestershire, Hunterston in Ayrshire, Hinkley Point in Somerset and at Trawsfynydd, Merionethshire. Reactors of the Magnox type were also ordered for Dungeness, Kent. The private construction companies building these power stations found themselves losing money in the process because of the new technology involved. Running costs were also exceeding estimates, so the AEA began building a prototype of a second generation power station, the Advanced Gas-cooled Reactor (AGR).

*1957* Sir Christopher Hinton left to become chairman of the Central Electricity Generating Board which centralised the powers of the old regional boards.

*1959* So far all reactors were of the 'thermal' type, which create less plutonium than the amount of uranium they use. That is, their 'conservation ratio' is less than 1. Now a new type of reactor was developed – the 'breeder' reactor which produced more fissile material than it consumed. This was called the fast-breeder reactor (FBR) or fast reactor: one of the first of this kind was started up at Dounreay, Scotland, in 1959. (A small one, able to produce enough electricity to light only four 25-watt bulbs had been run at Detroit at the beginning of the 1950s.) New and bigger FBRs later came into operation in Russia, France and the USA.

*1962* Up to the early 1960s, the facilities required in the UK for manufacturing and

In 1956, Queen Elizabeth switched on supply from the Calder Hall station. At the time this was claimed as 'another British First', but it turned out not to be so. In 1962 Calder Hall, which had supplied plutonium for military needs, was turned over mainly to electricity for the grid.

The first 'fast-breeder' reactor was started up at Dounreay in Scotland in 1959. The government research programme on fast-breeder reactors is now in question.

Bradwell, Essex. A Magnox station ordered after the Suez crisis.

reprocessing nuclear fuel for electricity generation were more or less identical to those required for the military programme. But in 1962 the military stockpile was large enough to enable Calder Hall and Chapelcross to be switched over mainly to electricity production, although exports of plutonium to the USA continued for another 20 years. The reactors may still be used to produce material for defence purposes as and when required.

*1964* Nuclear power went international again when, under the forerunner of the Organisation for Economic Co-operation and Development (OECD), the Dragon reactor started up at Winfrith, Dorset. This had been the brainchild of an eighteen-nation forum – the European Energy Authority (ENEA), set up in 1957 – and the Euratom Treaty of 1958 when eight European nations, not including the UK, agreed to pool resources. The Dragon was a High Temperature Gas-cooled Reactor (HTGR); the British paid for most of the running costs. 'The Dragon breathed its last' when its funds were cut off by the UK government, after it had operated for ten years. HTGRs built by other nations suffered a similar fate.

*1965* The Minister of Power announced the second phase of Britain's programme, the Advanced Gas-cooled Reactor. He and his advisors believed that this would lead eventually to the more efficient, low-cost version, the Mark III High-Temperature Gas-Cooled Reactor (HTGR). The first AGR station was built at Dungeness B, next to the Magnox, and was, like it, a twin reactor.

*1966* Frank Cousins, Labour Minister of Technology, announced a prototype FBR alongside the experimental one at Dounreay.

*1967* The British entered the heavy water reactor field (the type favoured by Canada) with a Steam Generating Heavy Water Reactor (SGHWR) prototype at Winfrith, Dorset. Two power stations of this kind were planned, but never built.

*The 1970s* were a period of re-evaluation for British nuclear power policies and programmes. No nuclear stations were ordered during the decade.

*1971* Since its formation, the AEA had been responsible for all aspects of the nuclear programme. Some of its functions were now split off – the main change being the formation of British Nuclear Fuels (BNFL), charged with producing all the fuel for British nuclear power stations and the export of uranium fuel to other countries.

*1973* The CEGB began to express a preference for the American PWR, which they described as 'a bread and butter system' compared with the AGR. Despite all the uncertainties, the CEGB now published proposals for a third nuclear programme of 18 large stations. The SSEB in Scotland planned to order a further eight, and each of these 26 stations would have two reactors.

*1974* Eric Varley, Labour Minister of Power,

decided, on the advice of the AEA, that plans to follow the route from Magnox to AGR to HTGR should be abandoned, and he cancelled the HTGR.

*1976* Another Labour Minister, Tony Benn, became Secretary of State for Energy and the AEA advised him that the next generation of stations should be PWR, not SGHWR. Benn countermanded the proposed SGHWR development, proposed two more AGR stations to keep the industry going, and encouraged progress with PWR development.

*1978* The United States government passed the Non-Proliferation Act which placed an embargo on the supply of enriched uranium to other countries.

*1979* The Conservative Party came to power. Later, the new Minister, Peter Walker, announced that he would like the CEGB to apply for the first British PWR station and also that he would like to see another new nuclear station ordered every year from 1982 to 1992. But by 1988 only one, Sizewell B, had been ordered.

Hinkley Point A, Somerset. Also ordered after Suez. A proposed PWR station is to be built alongside this Magnox station.

*1988* A new Minister of Power, Cecil Parkinson, announced that work on the experimental FBR at Dounreay would slow down and cease altogether in ten years' time. A disappointed AEA chairman described this type of fast reactor as 'the undisputed future for nuclear power' and 'the world's best bet for

Hunterston B in Ayrshire, Scotland. Magnox stations like this were admitted by the then Secretary of State for Energy to present 'major financial problems'.

Trawsfynydd, another Magnox station in Merionethshire in Wales.

providing electricity at competitive prices in the next century'.

Increasingly, as its own operations were scaled down by the government, the AEA looked to co-operating with Europe to fund research into future reactor types. These included the Joint European Torus (JET) fusion experiment at Culham, Oxfordshire. Another fusion project, the Next European Torus (NET) is on the drawing board in Germany, and there has been talk of a joint project using experience with the FBR.

One aspect of the nuclear debate has therefore been about the types of reactor which should be put into operation, and the British programme has been heavily criticised for consisting of too many prototypes. Another consideration has been whether Britain as a nation should go it alone in a high-tech industry whose origins were essentially international. It now looks as if Britain is, somewhat belatedly, reverting to an international, European approach to reactor design for the long-term future, while relying on an American design for the short term. This policy has been dictated by the high cost of development. The effect of this high cost, and the relative cost of other energy sources, is the subject of a later chapter.

The thirty years since the British first put nuclear power into the national grid has seen an investment of over $200 thousand million worldwide in nuclear power. Some 434 reactors are in operation; when those now on order come on stream, the total will exceed 500. The great majority are in West Europe, North America, the USSR and Japan, accounting for about 17 per cent of the world's electricity. The developing world trails behind – Argentina, Brazil, India, Pakistan, South Korea and Taiwan together have only 27 nuclear reactors between them, although in the latter two countries nuclear power accounts for a high proportion of the electricity generated.

The British contribution to the worldwide nuclear programme has therefore been modest, despite the enormous investment and

Magnox (Gas-Cooled Reactor)

These reactors use natural uranium metal, encased in a magnesium alloy can, as the fuel. This particular type of fuel reaches a maximum temperature of 400 degrees Celsius.

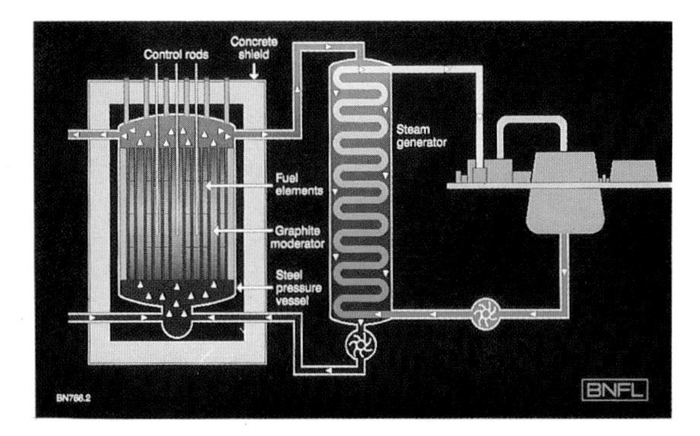

the Conservative government's commitment to the continued use of nuclear power in the electricity supply industry. France, by contrast, has concentrated on nuclear power and is now able to export electricity generated by this method. Sweden has said it will not use its nuclear power stations after the year 2010; faced with the problem of having to find an alternative means of producing half its electricity requirements, however, the Swedish government is having second thoughts. In the United States, where no orders for nuclear power stations have been placed since 1979, new nuclear stations may be ordered in the early 1990s to meet rising demand, but there is considerable public opposition to be overcome. There remain 110 operational stations with four more due to come on stream over the next three to four years. The Soviet Union has not slowed down its projected programme of nuclear power, but may do so. As for the Third World, the World Bank has ceased to advance loans to countries for the purpose of building nuclear plant.

Oldbury

The worldwide picture shows nuclear development in a somewhat confused position – there is no unanimity of view either amongst the experts or the politicians. It is against this background that the debate about the UK nuclear programme takes place.

AGR (Advanced Gas-Cooled Reactor)

These reactors use uranium oxide pellets in stainless steel cans assembled in graphite. Because of the design of the fuel, the maximum temperature is 660 degrees Celsius. This higher fuel temperature increases the amount of energy that can be extracted from uranium.

PWR (Pressurised Water Reactor)

These reactors use uranium dioxide encased in a zirconium can as the fuel. The design of the reactor is very compact, making it ideal for marine use. The fuel reaches a maximum of 324 degrees Celsius.

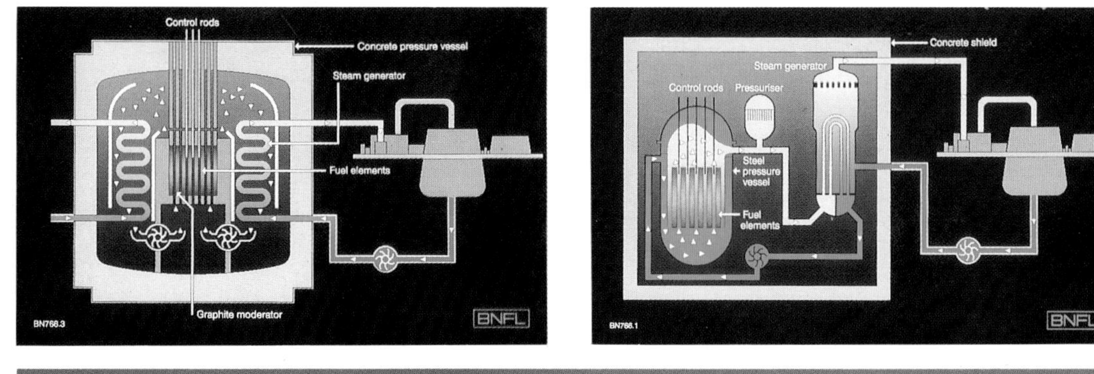

# 3. THE CYCLE

The so-called nuclear fuel cycle consists of the following elements:

(i) Manufacture of fuel to be used in a power station to generate electricity.
(ii) Reprocessing of spent fuel to remove the waste products and yield uranium and plutonium.
(iii) Recycling of uranium and plutonium to make new fuel which can be returned for use in the power station.

The key to the cycle lies in the nuclear core of the power station, where fuel rods filled with uranium pellets are used to begin the process of producing heat.

There are seven main stages in the cycle:

(1) Uranium is mined in various parts of the world – but not the United Kingdom. Mining has been going on for many years: Germany was extracting uranium (not for nuclear purposes) as far back as the 1930s. While there are now no significant reserves in Germany, there appear to be plenty elsewhere – in the United States (the largest), Canada, Australia, various parts of Africa, Sweden and France. Indeed world production in 1981 was more than double the level of consumption, resulting in substantial stockpiles and lower prices. Fears of a uranium shortage have therefore receded, and Britain has ensured continuity of supply by diversified buying policies and some involvement in mining companies overseas.

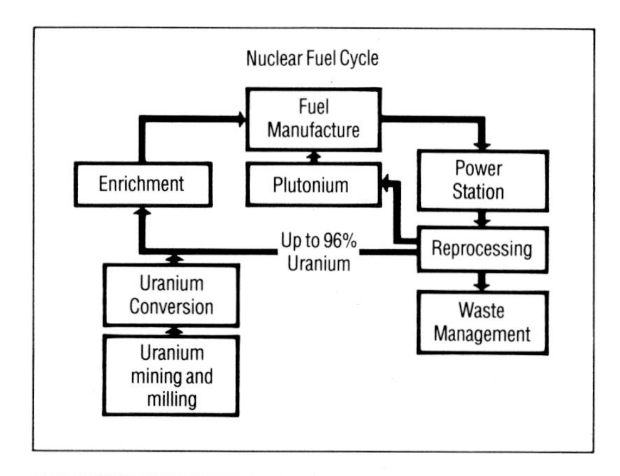


(2) When the ore has been extracted – it contains only a fraction of one per cent of uranium – it is put through a mill and ground to a fine 'sand', from which solvents dissolve out the uranium. The resultant material, called yellowcake, contains about 85 per cent uranium by weight. The uranium mine may produce 250,000 tonnes of ore in order to extract 1000 tonnes of yellowcake; the resultant waste or 'tailings' is radioactive.

(3) For most reactors – but not for the Magnox type – the yellowcake is then converted to uranium hexafluoride ('hex' for short) by further processing.

(4) The raw hex contains 0.7 per cent of U235 and, apart from the Magnox type, most power stations require fuel with 2 to 3 per cent of U235. It is therefore necessary to enrich the processed uranium by increasing the proportion of U235. Originally the United

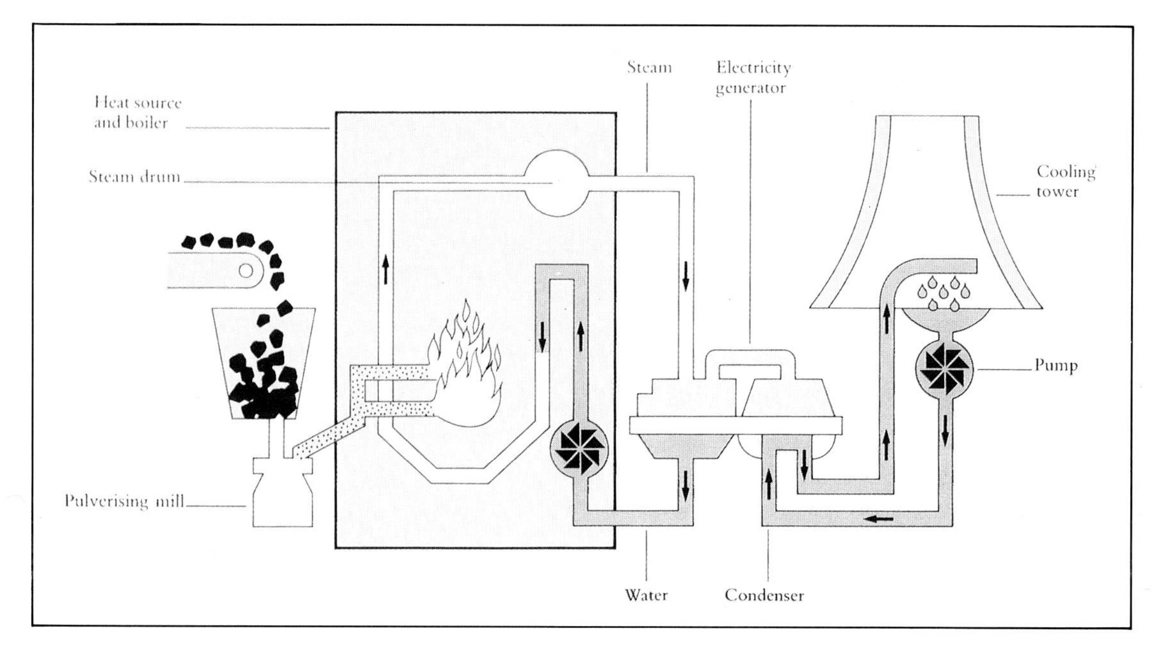


States had a monopoly of enrichment resources and during the 1970s supplied most of the enriched uranium used by 90 per cent of the world's nuclear power stations. The desire of European and other nations to achieve

A coal-fired power station

The only difference between a coal-fired power station and a nuclear power station is the method used to generate the heat to raise steam.

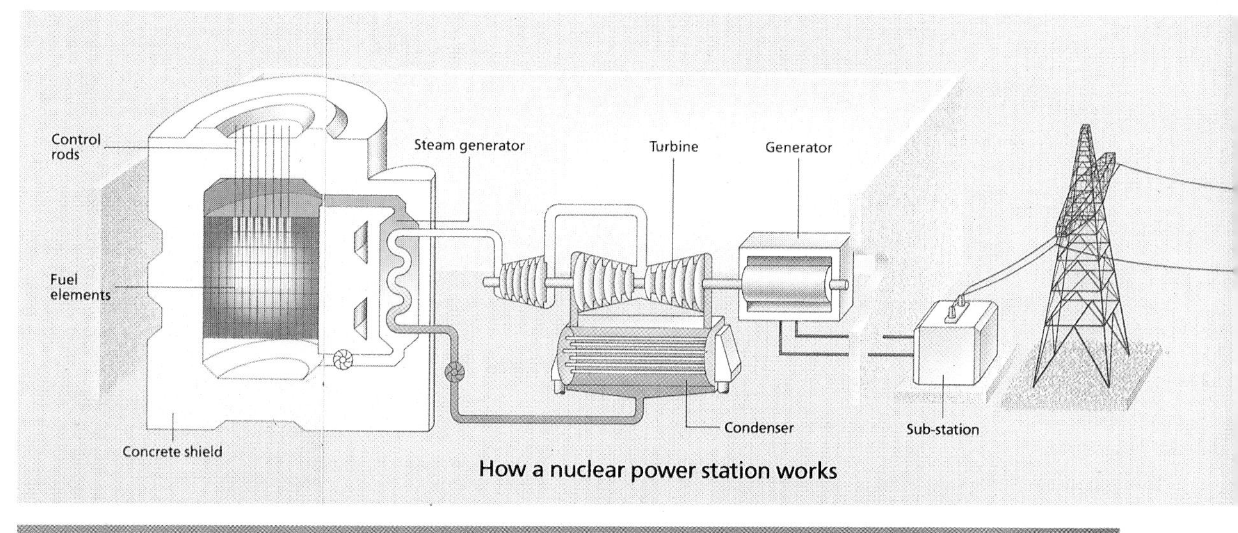


How a nuclear power station works

independence led to the development of capacity in France, Russia, China, West Germany, the Netherlands and in the UK, at the BNFL Capenhurst plant near Chester. At the latter, uranium in gaseous form is piped into a series of spinning centrifuges which revolve at very high speeds. These separate the U235 from the heavier U238. This centrifuge system is operated by BNFL in conjunction with German and Dutch partners through a joint European enterprise, URENCO.

(5) Once enriched, the uranium is transported to a fuel fabrication plant where it is made into a dioxide powder, then pressed into small pellets, sintered and loaded into stainless steel (or similar) tubes. A typical PWR fuel pin, as these tubes are called, would be 3.7m. long by 8mm. wide. AGR pins are shorter and fatter.

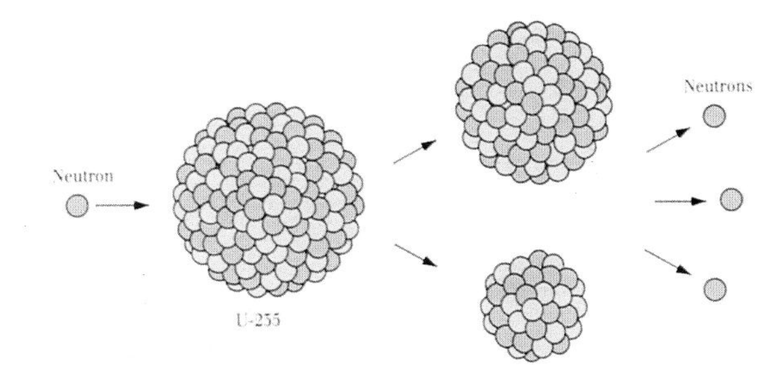


Natural uranium is a mixture of two main types, known as U-235 and U-238. When the nucleus of a U-235 atom absorbs a neutron (a nuclear particle) it splits into two smaller nuclei and releases energy and further neutrons (see above). This process, called nuclear fission, can be made to form a self-sustaining chain reaction in which each fission causes a further fission. It is in this way that uranium provides the energy for nuclear power.

Pressurised Water Reactor (PWR) fuel assembly at BNFL's Springfields Works, near Preston.

For magnox reactors, the yellowcake is chemically processed to yield uranium metal. This is formed into fuel rods which are inserted into cans made of a magnesium alloy.

(6) The fuel pins are assembled into bundles and placed in the reactor core and the fission process takes place. The heat produced is harnessed to turn water into steam, which turns a turbine connected to a generator, which generates electricity.

(7) In the fission process, a small proportion of uranium 238 is transmuted into plutonium 239 and there is also some unused uranium 235. Both of these are much too valuable not to be recycled. Therefore the spent fuel from a reactor is despatched to a special plant such as Sellafield for reprocessing. In the United States most fuel is simply stored, but both Britain and France have preferred to reprocess as part of their waste management strategy.

Reprocessing is the subject of much critical debate. The Windscale public inquiry of 1977, which sat for 100 days, the first major public inquiry on UK nuclear policy, investigated

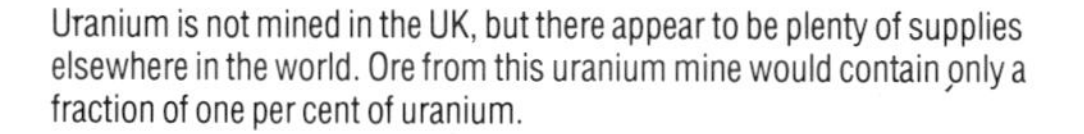

Uranium is not mined in the UK, but there appear to be plenty of supplies elsewhere in the world. Ore from this uranium mine would contain only a fraction of one per cent of uranium.

BNFL's application to build the Thermal Oxide Reprocessing Plant (THORP) at Sellafield. BNFL put forward the view that reprocessing was the safest and most efficient way of dealing with used fuel, as well as allowing valuable uranium and plutonium to be recovered. They needed THORP, they said, to enable them to deal with fuels from AGR and LWR stations.

Their intention was not only to service UK stations but also to reprocess fuels for overseas customers, particularly in western Europe and Japan. Critics represented at the inquiry – including local interests, Friends of the Earth, the British Council of Churches, Justice, The Town and Country Planning Association and the National Council for Civil Liberties – were particularly concerned about the safety aspects of reprocessing. Undoubtedly they were

BNFL's Springfields Works is the UK centre for the conversion of uranium ore concentrates into uranium metal and oxide and the manufacture of nuclear fuel elements. This picture shows an operator tipping concentrated uranium oxide into the dissolver tanks.

influenced in their attitude by the fact that reprocessing spent fuel had originally been developed in the United States in order to produce plutonium for the weapons programme. Among other issues, they questioned whether reprocessing was a sensible method of conserving energy sources, or whether this was both unnecessary and uneconomic because uranium from the mines was cheap and in such plentiful supply, so making the storage of spent fuel preferable. Mr Justice Parker, however, who conducted the 1977 inquiry, concluded that reprocessing did have economic advantages over storage.

The THORP plant at Windscale (now known as Sellafield) was given the go-ahead in 1978 after a House of Commons debate. It is expected to be reprocessing 700 tonnes of fuel a year by the 1990s.

BNFL's largest customers are the UK generating industry, all of whose fuel it produces and reprocesses. It has also developed export markets, supplying fuel or intermediate fuel products to Japan, Italy, Belgium, the Netherlands, Spain, West Germany and the USA, and it estimates that it now supplies 15 per cent of the world market for hex. In addition it reprocesses fuel for all these countries except the USA and Belgium, plus Sweden and Switzerland. Its order book for overseas reprocessing and transport is now worth over £4 billion, and in total it employs over 15,000 people. The commercial opportunities derived from reprocessing have therefore been considerable, and the long-term advantages appear to be highly attractive,

*(Above)* Final assembly of Magnox fuel elements at the Springfields Works. Over 4 million fuel elements have been manufactured at Springfields for the Magnox reactors built for the UK's first nuclear power programme. In addition, all the fuel for the five Advanced Gas-cooled Reactors now in operation has been manufactured at Springfields.

Uranium is enriched in the fissile isotope U235 in centrifuges like these at BNFL, Sellafield.

although dependent on the extent of the demand both domestically and overseas.

The case in favour of reprocessing rests, in part, on the fact that it eases the problem of radioactive waste disposal (more of this later). Moreover, recovered uranium and plutonium can be recycled for use in reactors, which effectively means that over 90 per cent of the spent fuel can be recycled. Reprocessing is thus advocated as a method of reducing the costs of the nuclear power process, particularly if and when uranium prices rise and supplies are in short supply. In a fast reactor programme, the recycling of uranium is the key factor, allowing up to 60 times as much energy to be produced from a given quantity.

The French, Germans and British always argued that reprocessing was a necessary step in the introduction of fast reactors. In fact, in Britain, future funding for research on these has recently been severely curtailed, although there is European collaboration in fast reactors in which the UK participates. In the short term, the critics of reprocessing may reasonably claim to have won some ground in Britain.

Thorp – the Thermal Oxide Reprocessing Plant – under construction at Sellafield.

At this point, before discussing the specifics of safety, it may be helpful to turn to the much broader environmental considerations. Public perception of these puts them at the top of the list of issues which must be addressed.

# 4. THE ENVIRONMENT

For all the millions of words that have been published and spoken about the world's environmental problems, it remains a fact that scientific understanding of the causes of acid rain, the greenhouse effect (global warming) and the destruction of the ozone layer is as yet imperfect – and certainly there is no consensus of opinion. Despite this, the public has demanded action – and politicians have agreed. This costs money.

Programmes to combat acid rain alone were expected to cost the British taxpayer more than £2 billion over a ten-year period, with 'further substantial expenditure' in the effort to cut sulphur dioxide and nitrous oxide emissions, mainly from coal-fired power stations. More recently, it has been proposed that a cheaper solution – gas-fired stations and imported low-sulphur coal – be adopted instead.

The problem of the greenhouse effect is much more intractable because there is no way to eliminate carbon dioxide emissions – its main single cause – from the coal-burning process. Natural gas is one alternative fuel which produces less carbon dioxide than coal and oil. Described by Lord Marshall as 'this gift of pure methane from God', natural gas was long reserved for domestic and other premium purposes, rather than for power generation. Now it is in surplus and, according to Lord Marshall, 'market forces dictate its consumption, not its preservation' so the supply industry will be, he says, 'a most vigorous exploiter of natural gas for electricity generation'. Coal, however, remains the major source of electricity generation in Britain today and will be so for many years; its environmental problems remain unsolved.

The coal industry has not been ready to accept the criticism that the UK's coal-fired power stations are a major contributor to global warming. British Coal says that while it is true that carbon dioxide contributes about half of the 'greenhouse gas' emissions, the other half is non-carbon dioxide gases such as CFCs which 'are much more serious because their average lifetime in the atmosphere is some ten times greater than carbon dioxide.' Furthermore, according to British Coal's chairman, Sir Robert Haslam, coal burning is responsible for only 15 per cent of the total British contribution and coal-fired power stations contribute just 7 per cent. This figure is supported by the World Coal Institute. Britain's emissions account for only 3 per cent of total global warming according to expert calculations.

Sir Robert says the proposition that nuclear power is environmentally-friendly is 'flawed' because replacing coal by nuclear power throughout the world is impractical. Action in Britain alone, or action concentrated only on coal, would be quite ineffective, he says. 'Annual consumption of coal in Britain is only 115 million tons out of a worldwide consumption of over 3 billion tons. This means the UK coal-powered stations contribute less

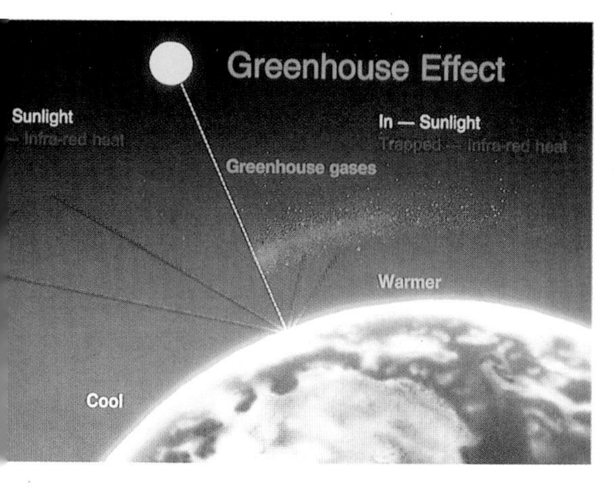


Sunlight passes through the air and, on reaching the ground, turns into heat. Certain gases including water vapour act as a 'blanket', preventing some of this heat escaping back into space – rather like the glass in a greenhouse. The amount of heat that is trapped depends on the quantity of 'Greenhouse' gases in the atmosphere, and it is their presence that helps keep the Earth comfortably warm – without it we would freeze. With too much gas trapped, the temperature will rise, resulting in global warming.

than one half per cent of the total global greenhouse effect.' The World Coal Institute agrees, asserting that there is 'an unfortunate tendency to put the blame too heavily upon coal'.

If British action to reduce carbon dioxide emissions from coal-fired power stations will be relatively ineffective in solving this worldwide problem, what is the answer? Sir Robert is clear that 'any action on the greenhouse effect must be international and all-embracing.' He advocates action on CFCs (which are already banned in some countries), policies on deforestation (which is responsible for 13 per cent of the global warming problem) and, most of all, improvements in the efficiency of energy use. One route to increased efficiency is the so-called FBC (fluidised-bed combustion) coal technology, now being developed in various parts of the world.

Critics react to these proposals by the coal lobby by saying that they are too little and too late. Lord Marshall was one of these critics: he is convinced that the solution to environmental problems is not improved use of coal, but increased use of nuclear power. This view was supported by the then Secretary of State for the Environment, Nicholas Ridley, who told TV viewers in October 1988 that:

> There is no doubt that if we want to arrest the greenhouse effect we should concentrate on a massive increase in nuclear generating capacity. Nuclear power stations give out no sulphur dioxide or carbon dioxide. They are the cleanest form of power.

The public, he added, could not have it both ways – 'nuclear power is the price to pay for cleaning up the atmosphere.' There was a good deal of support for this view – the *Daily Telegraph* for example wrote that 'Pollution-free nuclear power is our only answer against a sweltering existence.' The *Economist* agreed: 'Any programme to stop global warming will almost certainly have to include a large expansion of nuclear power. This is awkward for many greens whose first and deepest sentiment is a hatred of nuclear power.'

Lord Marshall has carried the environmental argument in favour of nuclear power still further by extending it from the national into the global context. The Third World should not be denied a chance to improve its living standards, he argues. For that, it needs fossil fuels and these are in diminishing supply. As the Third World's population explodes, so more fuel is needed. It therefore follows that industrialised countries should acquire more nuclear capacity in order to release fossil fuels to the developing world.

It could be argued that if fossil fuels, particularly coal, are a danger to the world environment, then there is little to be gained by transferring their use from the rich North to the poor South. And if it is true that a reduction in the number of coal-fired stations in one country would have little effect on environmental problems worldwide, then an agreed international programme is the only route which can be followed. This has, after all, been accepted as the right way to attack the proliferation of CFCs. Once again, the scientists are not unanimous about the causes of environmental problems, so the solutions offered sometimes appear to contradict each other.

The UK government's policy is clearly in support of some nuclear power element in the total energy 'mix' because it is said to be the most environmentally attractive solution to energy problems. One eminent scientist, however, disputes this. He is Sir Alan Cottrell, former Chief Scientific Advisor to the government and a member of the UK Atomic Energy Authority for many years until his retirement in 1987. He accuses the UK

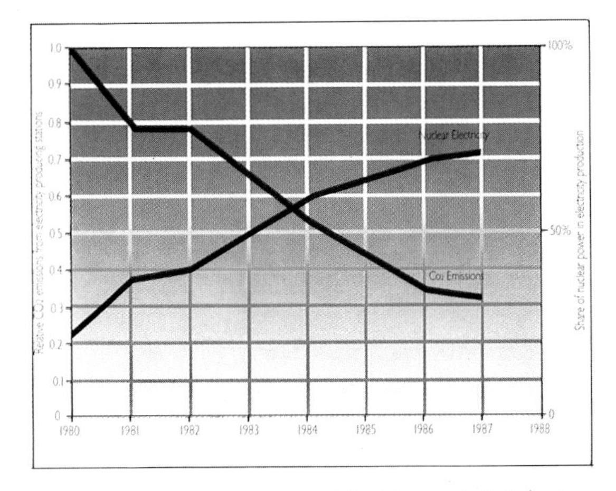


This graph shows that as the proportion of electricity generated in France by nuclear power increased, French carbon dioxide emissions decreased.

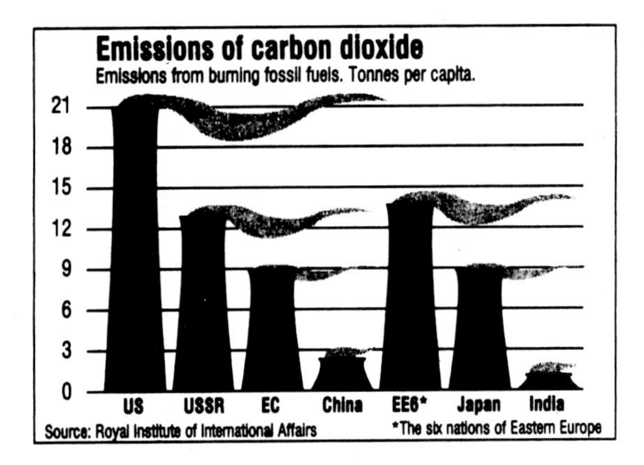


The Greenhouse Effect is a global problem and as such requires a global solution. No one country, not even the USA, which is responsible for much of the world's Greenhouse gas emissions, or the USSR, which is also a major contributor, can solve it. Moreover, the developing countries with their rapidly increasing populations cannot be expected to accept severe restrictions on their often very low standards of living. The developed countries, and that includes the UK, will therefore have to take the lead.

government of sabotaging the long-term efficiency of nuclear power. His argument is as follows. All thermal reactors, he says, use uranium so inefficiently that only the richest ore deposits are able to fuel them economically. Worldwide, these deposits amount to an energy resource only about half that of the world's oil, and so will very quickly be consumed if everyone turns strongly to nuclear power in preference to the environmentally dangerous fossil fuels. Sir Alan believes that 'it is quite possible by 2030 and virtually certain by 2050 that any remaining PWR stations will then have to stand idle because of prohibitively expensive (uranium) costs.'

Sir Alan claims that 'it has been well understood since the earliest days of nuclear energy that the ultimate methods for power generation were the fast breeder reactor and fusion because these can provide virtually infinite energy sources.' 'An FBR can use uranium 60 times more effectively than a PWR,' he says. 'Very low grade (uranium) ores can supply it (the FBR) and these are far more

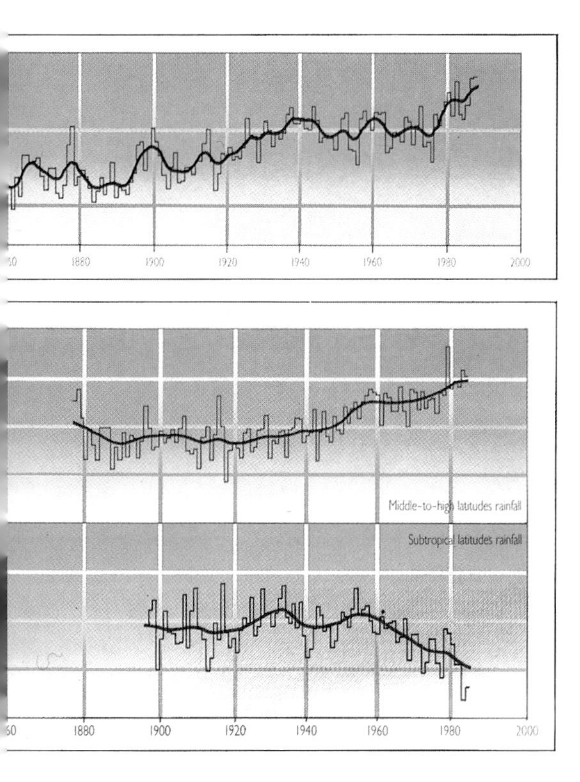


Something seems to be happening to our weather. Average world temperatures have generally increased over the last century. Seven of the warmest ten years since records began to be kept in the 1850s have been in the last decade, with 1988 followed by 1987 being the two hottest. Even so, it is impossible to say for certain that increasing amounts of Greenhouse gases are the cause.

abundant, measured as energy sources for FBRs, than the world's coal resources. The future for fusion power stations is unlimited.'

The government's attitude to nuclear power 'no longer makes sense,' says Sir Alan, because 'it has structured the privatisation of the electricity supply industry in a way that will cripple its research and development facilities' and, secondly, because 'it has cut the fast breeder reactor development programme and made a draconian cut in its funding of fusion energy research.' Even before these cuts, Sir Alan notes, Japan was spending ten times the UK figure on research into fusion energy. The AEA has also criticised the government's decision to cut the fusion research programme in which it was engaged.

If nuclear power is essential to meet mankind's needs for more electricity in the twenty-first century, then the case for it may be summed up as follows:

(1) While scientists have proved that high levels of radiation cause cancer, there is no evidence to prove a specific medical link between cancer and radiation and existing nuclear plant, although some claims have been made to this effect.
(2) Nuclear power presents no greater risk of accidents than other forms of modern technology even though the consequences of such an accident are terrible to contemplate.
(3) The problems of nuclear waste disposal are on the way to solution.
(4) There is no practical alternative to nuclear energy to fill the looming energy gap.
(5) Most significantly of all in the 1990s, nuclear is the most environmentally attractive energy alternative.

Some public perceptions are quite different. Using the term 'environment' in its widest context, some Green organisations believe that the UK government's current policies will lead to 'major environmental conflicts' and that the solution is a new and large-scale efficiency programme for electricity usage. They urge that the electricity industry, nuclear, non-nuclear and mixed as it is, should 'embrace environmental considerations into the heart of its strategic thinking.' They argue that even if nuclear power is environmentally friendly, it is simply impossible to build sufficient plant to meet our needs: other solutions are therefore unavoidable.

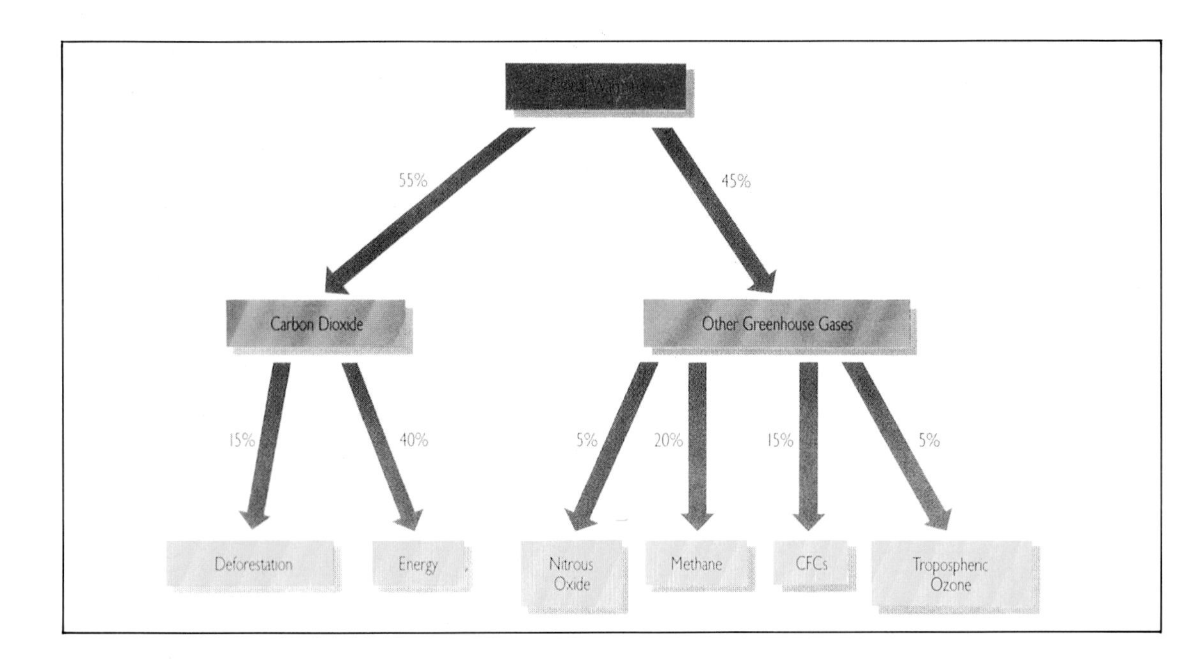


Causes of global warming

It is becoming increasingly recognised that a serious problem could arise from the emission of the Greenhouse gases. Unfortunately, because the earth's climate mechanisms are extremely complex, predictions of what could happen are very uncertain. Average temperatures could rise by between 1.5°C and 3.5°C within 50 years – very fast by natural standards. Such global warming could have far-reaching effects in terms of higher sea levels (as a result of thermal expansion and melting ice-caps and glaciers), altered rainfall patterns and extremes of weather. The increased carbon dioxide levels would affect plants. Some of the results of these changes could be: an increased number of storms, like the hurricanes in Jamaica in 1988 and 1989; flooding of low-lying land (estimates of sea level rise have varied from a few centimetres to a few metres); shifts in the food-growing areas and less security of supplies because of droughts and soil erosion in some areas and wetter conditions in others; extinction of some animal and plant species because they cannot accommodate to the rapidly changing conditions; loss of supplies of fresh water in some areas because of the changing pattern of rainfall. The effects would not be uniform and some regions would be affected more than others; some could end up as winners and some as losers. For example, the American corn belt could move further north, and parts of Russia that are frozen wasteland could become fertile agricultural land. Even the winners, however, would be likely to go through an uncomfortable period as they adapted to the new conditions, while the sufferings of the losers would outweigh any possible benefits.

A recent joint study for the CPRE and the FOE claimed that the electricity industry's plans for the future are 'set on an inevitable collision course with environmental and public interests' because the industry 'is obsessed by increased electricity demand.' While the supply industry believes that there will be difficulties in meeting demand in the early 1990s and that much new capacity will be required by the turn of the century, the Greens assert that 'electricity demand can be reduced at a fraction of the cost of obtaining new sources of supply.' 'So far,' they say, 'too little attention has been given to energy conservation in the UK. . . . An EEC-sponsored study has concluded that, across the country, energy equivalent to ten Sizewell B power stations is readily available for a fraction of the cost of nuclear, or any other supply side option' – by adopting conservation measures.

One technological solution to increased

efficiency, the Greens suggest, is to allow electricity generating companies to construct smaller, less obtrusive generating stations more quickly. Using existing technology, the changes they propose could allow electricity requirements to be reduced by half or more, they claim. 'Many of these measures would pay for themselves in less than two years.' These include changes in the design of ordinary domestic light bulbs, refrigerators and the motors used to drive electric appliances. More efficient insulation and other savings in the home are also recommended.

This is all very well, but it presupposes that, in a free society, the average citizen will make the environmentally correct choice. There is no evidence to support this. On the contrary, some incentive, usually of a financial kind, is often necessary if habits are to be changed. This was the case with lead-free petrol, where only a price-cut triggered a real increase in demand. The alternative is legislation, but a law to prohibit, say, use of suspect light bulbs is hardly viable in a society in which civil liberties are treasured.

In the Third World, the likelihood of a switch to the 'green' solution is even more improbable

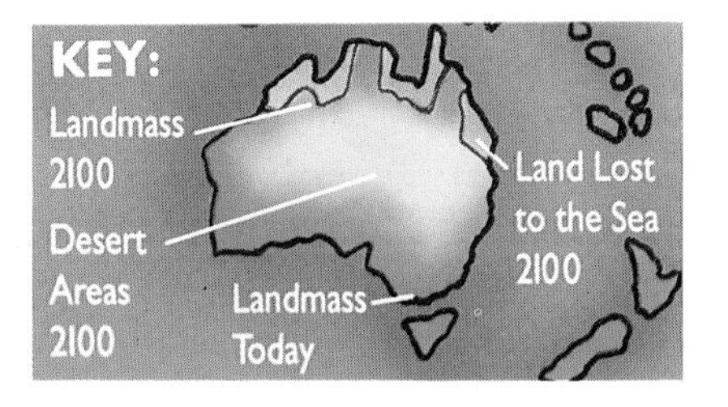


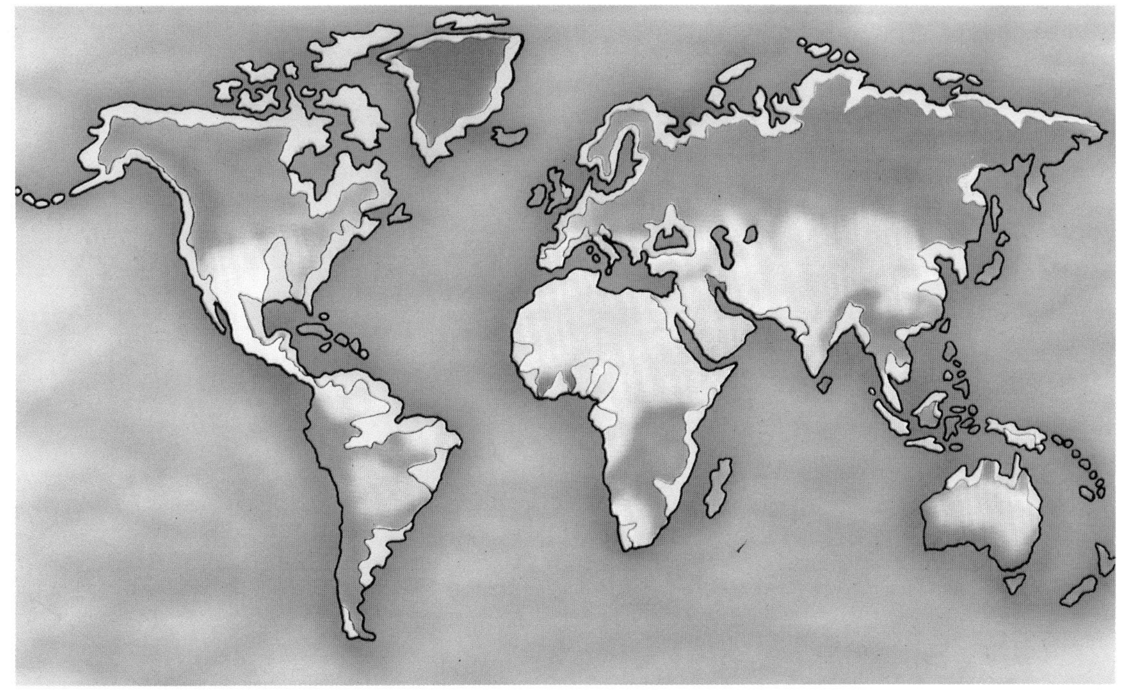

An artist's impression of how the world might look in the year 2100 if some predicted trends materialise..

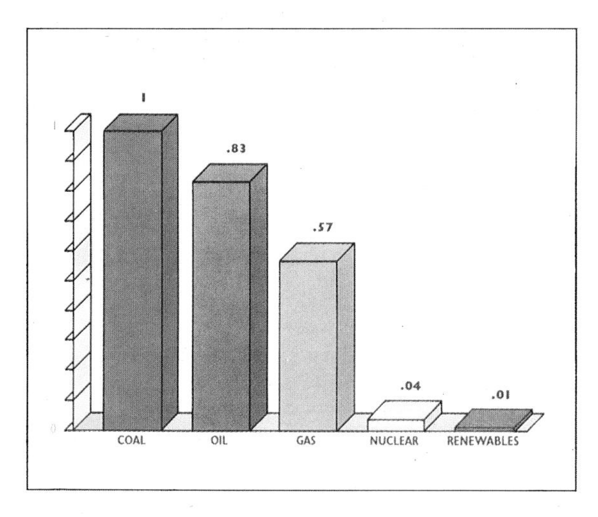


Natural gas emits only about 60% as much carbon dioxide as coal for the same energy output and so there would appear to be immediate benefit in using it in place of coal. Supporters of nuclear energy propose a massive increase in its use which would result in lower carbon dioxide emissions.

without a financial incentive, especially in the short term; by the longer term, the damage may be already done. China, for example, sits on one third of the world's known coal reserves; if these were suddenly to be exploited by the People's Republic in search of a higher standard of living, the environmental effects could be tragic.

Meanwhile, the nuclear industry itself continues to invest heavily to improve its own efficiency, including its environmental efficiency. British Nuclear Fuels is investing increasing amounts for research and development. Nirex is asking for large sums to

In addition to the worrying quantities of carbon dioxide emitted from a power station like Ferrybridge in Yorkshire (below), such coal-fired stations emit sulphur dioxide and nitrogen oxides which are causing the acidification of lakes and streams in Norway and Sweden and have been accused of causing damage to forests throughout Europe. At home, the acid rain damages lakes, rivers, forests and the fabric of historic buildings and the sensitive eco-systems of water areas.

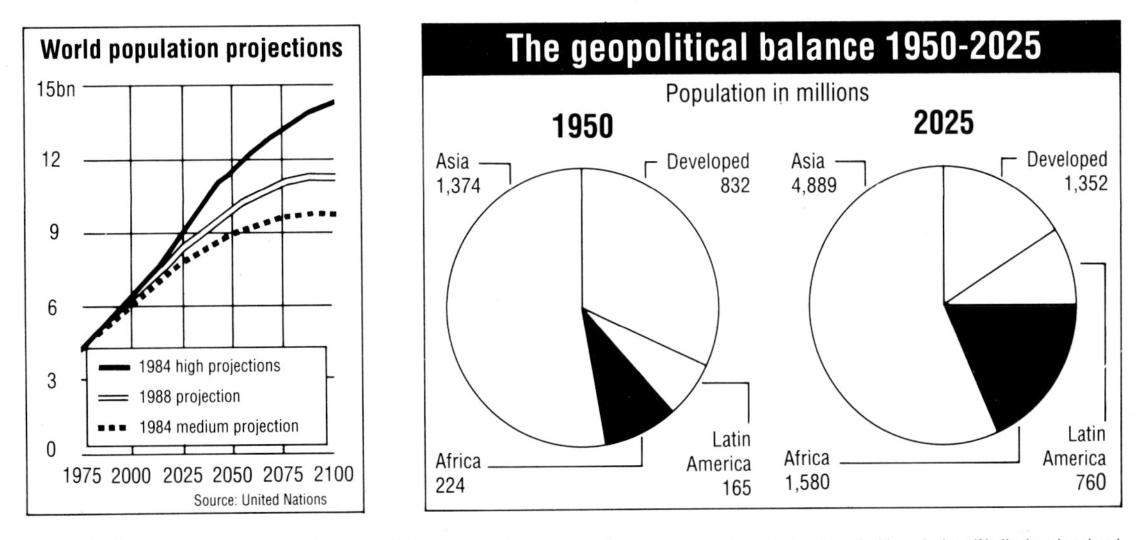


As the Third World expands relative to the Developed World, in terms of population growth, some proponents of nuclear power argue that the Developed World should use nuclear power so as to release fossil fuels for the Third World.

Nuclear power would reduce carbon dioxide emissions if it displaced coal and oil for electricity generation. However if nuclear power continues to grow at its present slow rate, it might be generating no more than a fifth of the world's electricity by 2020. Since carbon dioxide emissions are increasing, nuclear power's contribution would be only a part of the total solution.

be invested in the forms of waste disposal and storage for which it is responsible. If improvements in these and other key areas, particularly environment-related areas, can be made by the industry, then their case for a restoration of government support for advanced forms of research and development will be that much stronger. This research centres on the fast breeder reactor and, on a longer term basis, on fusion reactors. If these are as environmentally clean as their exponents maintain, there is a strong case for further development.

The head of the UK Meteorological Office has pointed out that it might well be ten years before scientists could conclusively prove that global warming is really occurring. If we wait for the proof before taking any action to mitigate its possible effects, it may well be too late, and the result could be catastrophic. If global warming is taking place we need to know its causes now. Meanwhile, it is argued, we must take out an insurance policy by replacing coal-fired stations with nuclear stations now. But, as the Greens have pointed out, such a world-wide replacement programme would necessitate the construction of one nuclear power station every day for the next ten years. Clearly this is impracticable. We all want to improve the environment, but we are far from agreed about the cost of doing so, or how to spend the money.

At the beginning of this chapter, reference was made to a £2 billion plan to cut emissions of sulphur dioxide and nitrous oxides from British power stations, in order to meet the EEC's legislative requirements for a better environment. Once the supply industry was to be privatised, this cost seemed too great for its new owners to bear. The programme, including fitting flue gas desulphurisation plants (or FGDs), was abandoned except at Drax power station, although the Prime Minister, Mrs Thatcher, told a meeting of the Royal Society in 1990 that 'We will have to do it on others.' The industry's preferred alternative was to import low-sulphur coal, use more gas-fired technology, and generally spread out the FGD programme over a much longer time-scale. The Greens consider this a violation of EEC agreements and believe that new, harsher targets should be set, similar to those already imposed on Germany, the Netherlands, France and Belgium. Thus even those programmes which the industry had agreed to put into effect are now the subject of a hot debate between the environmentalists and those legally responsible for their implementation.

Friends of the Earth use these two diagramatic illustrations to show how the demand for more and more electricity supply affects the environment in a number of ways. Most power stations are obtrusive by their nature. The large power stations which are central to the industry's current strategy must be located on the coast, lakes or rivers, since they need large quantities of cooling water. Nuclear stations are deliberately placed in relatively remote locations. Power lines can damage vast tracts of countryside. Consequently, areas of great natural beauty and interest – even those designated for their special landscape or wildlife value – may be threatened by their presence. Power station construction may take up to 10 years, and irrevocably alter the character of local communities.

11,000,000 tonnes carbon dioxide
16,000 tonnes sulphur dioxide
29,000 tonnes nitrogen oxides
1,000 tonnes dust

The annual environmental impact of a modern coal-fired power station – output 1,800 mw

5,000,000 tonnes of coal
300,000 tonnes of limestone*
NEEDS: 1,200,000,000 cubic metres warm water
80 hectares of rural land on coast or river site, plus 90 hectares during construction
* assumes continuing use of the limestone/gypsum FGD process

21,000 tonnes sludge
500,000 tonnes gypsum*
1,000,000 tonnes ash

The annual environmental impact of a modern nuclear power station – output 1,150 mw

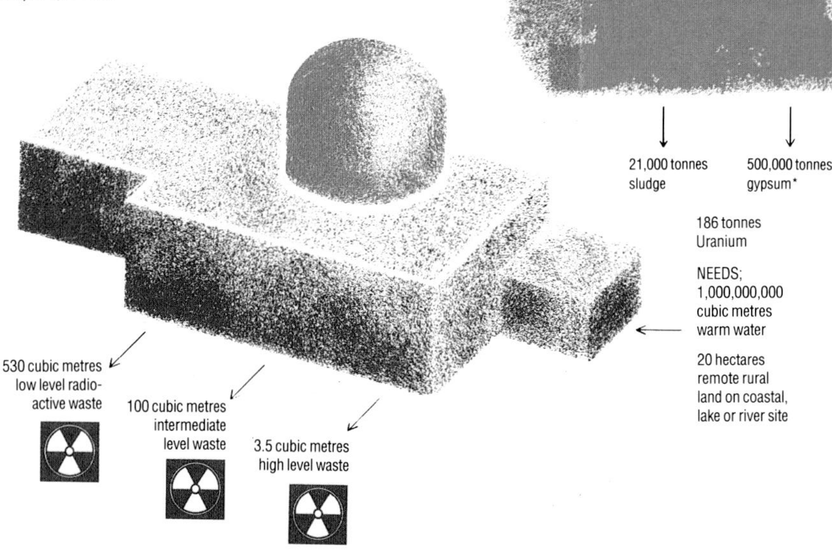

# 5. COSTS

If nuclear power is part of an environmentally attractive package to meet UK energy needs, is it economically as well as environmentally viable?

For years, the British public was told by politicians that nuclear power was the cheapest form of energy and, even if this was not the only reason for investing in it, then it was certainly the most acceptable politically. All the political parties, from the earliest days, were broadly supportive about the long-term cost benefits, yet the exact cost advantage had always been vague. Back in 1965, when the Central Electricity Generating Board decided to support the AGR type of reactor, a Conservative MP asked the Labour Minister of Power to tell the House of Commons 'how much cheaper this base load power will be and what are the economic and technical advantages?' The Minister's reply was: 'I am sure we have hit the jackpot this time. . . . Here we have got the greatest breakthrough of all time.' Even the cautious *Financial Times* supported his view, calling nuclear energy 'pure gain for the British economy'.

Twenty years later such optimism was under considerable scrutiny. The *Sunday Times*, writing in the autumn of 1988, described British nuclear power stations as 'a costly embarrassment'. How had attitudes changed so much and what justification was there for this new criticism of nuclear energy on grounds of cost?

Costs have always been measured in comparison with other forms of power: for many years the CEGB view was that 'coal-fired stations are cheaper to build, but more expensive to run than nuclear power stations.' Later, it modified this view to the extent that it believed 'even on assumptions adverse to nuclear power, the Magnox stations do not add much more to system costs than the alternative coal and oil stations would have done. On less adverse assumptions, they reduce these costs significantly.'

Much depends on the price paid for coal. At the Sizewell inquiry into the proposal to build the first PWR station, the power supply industry forecast that coal prices would increase. This referred to coal from British pits, with whom the CEGB had an exclusive contract for supply – they could not buy foreign coal. Remember that the electricity industry depends for about 80 per cent of its supply on coal; the Sizewell inquiry was told:

> Whatever decisions are taken with regard to new plant over the next few years, the industry will continue, because of its existing plant mix, to be committed to coal as the major element of its fuel supplies beyond the end of the century.

Two factors caused this reliance on British coal to be re-evaluated. The first was the criticism of coal-fired stations on environmental grounds, and the second was the privatisation of the electricity supply industry. It should also be noted that the South of Scotland Electricity Board had stated that the AGR design of nuclear station, in particular,

Sizewell B. The first of the 'new generation' of PWR stations to be built in Britain and, at present, the only such station under construction.

while more expensive to build than either a coal-fired or a PWR nuclear station, was cheaper to run. It believed that the AGR system 'stands comparison in terms of economics and performance with any other system in the world.'

Cecil Parkinson, then Secretary of State for Energy, when reviewing the Sizewell inspector's report in March 1987, accepted the conclusion that 'building Sizewell B is likely to be a lower-cost option to meet capacity need than a new AGR or a new coal-fired power station.' In coming to this decision he would have taken into account the cost of making Sizewell B safe when it had outlived its working life – the expense of the so-called 'decommissioning' of the station, when the site has to be closed down in such a way as to be completely harmless to those living or working in the area. This is a long and expensive process.

The electricity supply industry takes a rather matter-of-fact view of the problems of decommissioning. It notes that it will 'continue to be responsible' for nuclear power stations which have reached the end of their useful lives 'until any hazard from radiation has been reduced to insignificance', while paying 'the most detailed attention to safety . . . right through to decommissioning'.

The sites themselves will continue to be valuable, it is claimed, because further use can be made of their existing facilities:

> Most of the plant can be dismantled in the normal way. . . . However, the reactor structure itself cannot be dismantled for some time. This structure takes up only 5 per cent of the total site and it will be sealed off for a number of years while the radioactivity decays.

In any case, 'dismantling the reactor will not commence until at least ten years after shut-down to allow the more intense activity to decay.' Thus power stations being built now will have to be dismantled by future generations who had no responsibility for their commissioning.

The general consensus is that decommissioning will be completed in three stages. The first and least expensive will entail removing the spent fuel, which would be sent to Sellafield for reprocessing. The reactor building would be locked and the plant isolated from the general public and kept under security guard. Stage two will be to dismantle and demolish all the fixed structures of the power station except the reactor building itself. The third stage will be to deal with the reactor.

One of the most respected critics of the UK nuclear industry, Walter Patterson, points out that this is the theory, but that 'no one anywhere has ever decommissioned a large power reactor after its normal working life' – although small research reactors and a handful of experimental power reactors have been closed, the latter being ones which were not in service for a long period. Since Patterson wrote these words, the Shippingport reactor in the USA has been decommissioned. Work has also begun at Berkeley, the Magnox station in Gloucestershire; this, like a similar plant at Chinon in France, is likely to be opened as an information centre and exhibition on the theme of decommissioning. AEA Technology is also currently decommissioning the Windscale demonstration AGR, a process which has been going on since 1981. As more sites come out of operation year by year it is likely, as Patterson forecasts, that there will be a good many moth-balled power stations by the early twenty-first century. In theory it would be possible to leave a redundant station moth-balled at stage one, since it would be less radioactive than an operational station which may be visited by the public on guided tours – but this would hardly be a politically acceptable solution to the problem of decommissioning.

This diagram illustrates the shape of the electricity supply industry after privatisation. Two private companies, National Power and Power Gen, have been set up to take over some of the functions of the former CEGB. Nuclear Electric remains a state concern, handling the nuclear power stations formerly controlled by the CEGB.

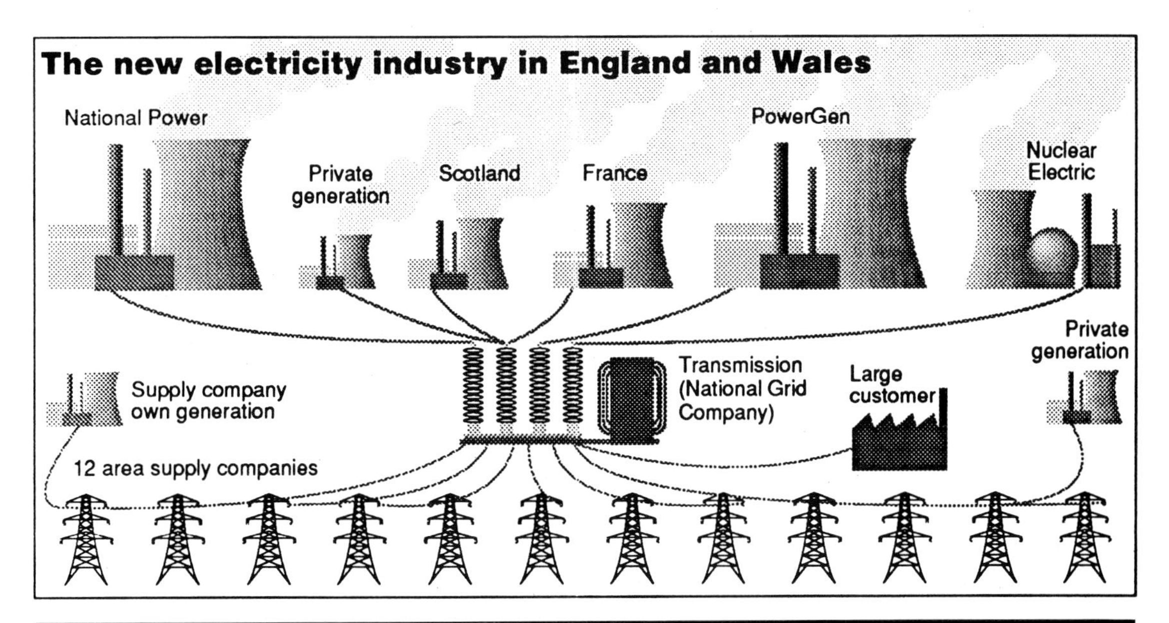

Berkeley nuclear power station in Gloucestershire, where the process of decommissioning has begun.

The debate about decommissioning has taken on a political colour since its cost became (inevitably) a factor in government plans for electricity supply generation. The government's decision in November 1989 to ease privatisation of the supply industry by forming two new state-owned companies to take over all the UK nuclear power stations was influenced, at least in part, by the unknown scale of decommissioning costs. The Greens have always feared that the decommissioning process would introduce new dangers to the environment, but the fact is that plants inevitably need to be shut down and decisions must be taken about what to do with them. These decisions cannot be delayed indefinitely. The industry's attitude is that the best engineering practices will enable them to decommission in an entirely safe way, even if the costs cannot always be easily forecast. Experience of actual decommissioning procedures is now being acquired: it is to be hoped that some of its mystique will be lost in the process.

These costs will, of course, be met by the electricity consumer in the final analysis, either as consumer or taxpayer. When the government put forward its proposals for privatising the supply industry there was, however, some criticism that investors in it would not find it attractive to take on all the costs of nuclear stations, particularly as these would include the somewhat unknown costs of decommissioning. In the event, Cecil Parkinson's last act before leaving his job as Secretary of State for Energy was to retain the Magnox stations in the public sector. He explained that 'the costs for the Magnox stations, which have now become clear, would present major financial problems' for the private power supply companies. 'They can only be paid for by the customer or the taxpayer. The Government does not believe that this legacy of the past should be borne by customers in the future.' He was referring to the period up to the year 2002 when the last Magnox station would be closed, leaving the private sector controlling the AGR and PWR stations.

A levy of 10 per cent on the consumer's electricity accounts was put forward as the most satisfactory way of raising money to finance the nuclear programme and research into renewable sources. Later, in answer to the problems of privatisation, Mr Parkinson's successor transferred all nuclear stations to the public sector.

Meanwhile, the need to control emissions from coal-fired stations was itself threatening to increase their costs. Critics of coal-fired stations point out that even the most modern existing stations are environmentally unfriendly. One such station annually produces the following waste products: 10.8 million tons of carbon dioxide, 0.8 million tons of ash, 0.2 million tons of sulphur dioxide and a large quantity of hydrochloric acid. In addition, it emits to the atmosphere a wide range of trace elements such as lead, arsenic, and zinc. The critics say that about 2000 people die prematurely each year in the UK, because of pollution from all the coal-fired stations. The cost of modifications is considerable, as we have already noted.

One such programme, to purchase equipment to remove sulphur dioxide from the smokestack of the UK's largest conventional power station, at Drax, has been quantified as likely to add 8 per cent to the cost of producing its electricity, a cost which will be charged on to the consumer as a levy. This will not lessen the demand from the public for environmental improvement, although Greens will argue that these costs could be offset by more efficient use of electricity itself.

For the future, National Power, one of the two new private generating companies which took over from the CEGB, says its coal and oil-fired power stations will be equipped with flue gas desulphurisation (FGD) plant, which reduce sulphur emission by 90 per cent. 'Special burners are also on the way to reduce the emission of nitrogen oxides by an estimated 30 per cent by the turn of the century. Carbon dioxide emissions are also decreasing through continuing improvements in thermal efficiency.' In all, say National Power, their emissions-control programme will cost over £1.5 billion. There was some controversy about who should pay for the FGD plant (called 'Scrubbers' in popular parlance), as neither National Power nor Power-Gen would want their shareholders to be saddled with the cost. In the end it will probably be the public at large – either as consumers or taxpayers – who will pay up. As already noted, lower-cost alternatives are being proposed, involving the use of gas or low-sulphur coal.

From **The Fourth Report from The Energy Committee (House of Commons 1990)**

We wish to make clear at the outset that it is not possible at present to put forward a particular figure as the cost or price of nuclear power, for a number of reasons. First, Britain has three different types of reactor (one not yet in service), and the costs of each are different and are sensitive to different influences. Secondly, capital costs are a major part of the cost of nuclear power, and different accounting conventions can drastically affect total costs; in particular the use of historic costs (not adjusted for inflation) as opposed to current costs can have a huge effect on the figures, as we discovered in respect of the Scottish reactors. Thirdly, the rate of return required on capital can vary from one period to another and according to the 'risk environment' (for example a competitive as opposed to a monopolistic market), and this too has a major impact on the figures. Fourthly, many nuclear costs, notably those of decommissioning and waste disposal, are extremely long-term and cannot be measured now with any certainty.

Another major factor affecting the economics of nuclear power is that the costs of fossil-fired generation have fallen appreciably, mainly due to lower world market prices for fossil fuels in the wake of the collapse in the oil price from early 1986. The currently low price of gas, combined with a change in policy allowing this premium fuel to be used for power generation, makes the use of gas by far the cheapest option for generation at the present time, irrespective of any perceived change in the cost of nuclear power.

The nuclear industry has a long history of over-optimistic forecasts and that the objectors at the Sizewell B Public Inquiry predicted the likely construction cost more accurately than the CEGB itself. According to a paper prepared on behalf of National Power in October 1989, when the cost of Sizewell B had already risen 26 per cent above the estimate presented by the CEGB at the Inquiry, 'further unbudgeted cost increases must be expected'.

At our request the SSEB provided figures using current costs — 5.879, 3.152 and 5.161p/kWh for the three reactors, indicating a weighted average of 4.385p/kWh. These were based on 'net asset value' (i.e. depreciated replacement cost) rather than gross replacement cost. Furthermore they do not reflect the increases likely to be caused by fixed price contracts with BNFL. The figures are therefore consistent with what is known of costs in England and Wales, bearing in mind that Scotland has had better operating experience with its AGRs and the better English AGRs would show 'very similar costs'.

Another economic argument against the use of more coal-fired power stations is that world supplies of coal are finite and there is a big demand for their use in chemical and other industries which manufacture coal-based products. Why burn it if it is useful and already becoming scarce and therefore more expensive? The same argument is applied to oil. Uranium, on the other hand, has virtually no use in manufacture.

The debate about the relative costs of nuclear and coal-fired stations is not a simple one, nor are all the facts about the costs of environmental pollution fully understood. A major change in British government policy on nuclear power was made in November 1989, when it became clear that the privatisation of the electricity supply industry could not take place unless the nuclear element was separated from the supply chain, because of the difficulty of forecasting the cost of nuclear power. John Wakeham, who had succeeded Cecil Parkinson as Secretary of State for Energy, told the House of Commons that 'the Government have for some time recognised that our nuclear power is more costly than power from fossil-fuelled generating stations. . . . The preparations for privatisation have revealed substantially increased costs, relating primarily to the Magnox stations.' Following his statement, not only was a new nuclear company set up, but the plans to build new PWR stations beyond Sizewell B were suspended. In 1990, Greenpeace produced a report examining the costs of British nuclear power which recommended wholesale closure on economic grounds alone.

Nonetheless decisions may still have to be made about the design of generating plant for the future. Nuclear power may be costly, but it may also be the most environmentally attractive. Yet closely allied to public concern about the environment is concern about the relative safety of nuclear power. This is the subject of the following chapters.

Costs of nuclear power came to the forefront of the debate once more following the Minister's decision, later in 1989, to take the nuclear programme out of the privatised supply industry — on the grounds that new information had come to light about the economics of nuclear stations, including the new PWR station at Sizewell. This decision was subject to the close scrutiny of the House of Commons all-party Energy Committee, which met early in 1990 and reported in June that year. One of its conclusions was that if further nuclear investment proved to be justified in 1994, on the grounds of diversity of supply or reduced pollution, the full costs (and this included 'social' costs and 'risk' costs) should be made public prior to the decision being taken.

As the Commons Committee report was being published, Nuclear Electric, the state-owned body set up to control the existing nuclear stations in England and Wales, including Sizewell B, the only new PWR station now being built, declared that the latter's completion 'is fully justified by its costs'. It reported that its own review of the project showed Sizewell 'still expected to produce electricity at costs in the range 3.4 to 4.1 p/kWh'or at a higher rate of return on capital, '4.8 to 5.7 p/kWh. These figures can be compared with estimates of 3.5 to 4.5 p/kWh for a new coal-fired station.' This was despite the fact that the government had decided to cut the programme from four PWR stations to one.

However Lord Marshall, head of the supply industry from 1982 to 1989, and now in what he described as an 'independent position' as Chairman of the World Association of Nuclear

Operators, saw the government decision to defer or abandon the PWR programme as one which would not allow the industry to survive. 'That is not because nuclear power is uneconomic,' he said, 'but because the [economic] benefits of nuclear power — assuming you get everything right — come in the long term, not in the short term.'

Marshall declared that, for the same reason, 'Britain under the new privatised power system is unable to build big coal-fired power stations'. Instead, it will build 'cheap gas turbines that burn expensive fuel. When the gas runs out, our electricity supply system wil become insecure (and) some new form of long-term obligation will be introduced by a wiser government, and our coal industry and our nuclear industry can be revived again . . . The solution to the problem of greenhouse warming will need a massive investment in nuclear power.'

| US COSTS – CENTS | OPERATIONS | | MAINTENANCE | | TOTAL | |
|---|---|---|---|---|---|---|
| | Nuclear | Coal | Nuclear | Coal | Nuclear | Coal |
| 1982 | 0.48 | 0.13 | 0.33 | 0.24 | 0.81 | 0.37 |
| 1986 | 0.73 | 0.15 | 0.47 | 0.26 | 1.20 | 0.41 |
| (c/kWh) | | | | | | |

Critics complain that the British choice of many different designs of station has inevitably led to a costly nuclear programme. France and the United States, which have concentrated on a single type – light water reactors – should therefore show an improvement. However Greenpeace maintains that the figures above show that even in the USA the operations and maintenance costs of nuclear plants were nearly three times those of coal-fired plants by 1986 – and rising.

His last point seemed to meet with approval of the new supply industry. Mr Baker, chief executive of the largest of the two companies, National Power, which had earlier been expected to control the nuclear stations, predicted that his organisation would be back in the nuclear power business within 50 years. 'There is no credible way through the next half century without it and it will be the electricity companies who will be involved,' he said.

From **The Fourth Report from The Energy Committee (House of Commons 1990)**

It may be possible to justify further nuclear investment in 1994 despite the currently unfavourable economics of nuclear power. **However, we regard it as essential that in doing so the economics of nuclear power are in no way glossed over, that the full costs and risks of nuclear power are ascertained as closely as possible, and that this analysis be fully exposed to public examination prior to decisions being taken. In that way, the cost of diversity of supply and reduced pollution can be made clear, and, more importantly, the cost of achieving diversity of supply and reduced pollution by means of nuclear power can be compared with the cost of achieving the same ends by other means.** Such means could include renewable energy or (in the case of pollution) greater energy efficiency, as we have argued elsewhere.

The circumstances which gave rise to this Report might never have occurred if more information about the costs of nuclear power had been publicly available. Given the recent history of nuclear power it will never again be possible to take assurances as to the viability of any type of nuclear power on trust. The transfer of the nuclear stations to separate companies and the segregation of nuclear and other operations in Nuclear Electric's accounts will not necessarily result in sufficiently detailed information for the changing nature of those costs to be monitored. We are encouraged therefore by the Department's belief that 'it is desirable that full information about the costs and prices of nuclear power, and indeed of power from other sources, is made publicly available'. **We regard this as an undertaking. We recommend that, in fulfilling this undertaking, the Department ensures that annual reports on nuclear generation costs for Magnoxes, AGRs and (eventually) Sizewell B are published in a form analogous to the CEGB's Grey Books, and that information be provided in the same form both for Scotland and for England and Wales.** Since nuclear power will be trading in an artificial market and will be subsidised by both consumers and taxpayers, there can be no argument for commercial confidentiality, and **we will have no hesitation in using our power to send for papers if we consider that the information provided by Nuclear Electric or SNL is inadequate.**

# 6. SAFETY

Marie Curie, the wife of Pierre Curie who discovered the properties of radium, continued to work with it after his death in 1920. So did her daughter. Both later died of cancer, attributed to their work. (Pierre Curie's death was not caused by cancer – he was knocked down by a horse-drawn dray.) The story of the two women's courage was so widely known

Marie and Pierre Curie with their daughter Irene in 1905. Both mother and daughter died from radiation effects.

that the risk of death by radiation was embedded in the European consciousness long before World War II, when the dropping of the first atom bomb brought the horror as well as the benefits of radiation to world-wide attention. The question that has dominated thinking since the 1970s is: How great is the danger of radiation from nuclear power?

Statistical analysis of risk may not convince everyone. The noted scientist Sir Fred Hoyle claimed a few years ago that the risk of death from living close to a nuclear power plant was statistically equivalent to 'driving the car for an additional 250 yards a day'. Another scientist who works in the nuclear industry says 'I have calculated I receive more extra radiation from a week spent in Cornwall, an area with a much higher level of natural background radiation than Oxfordshire, where I live, than I have accumulated in working at Harwell for ten years.'

Since radiation cannot be detected by the senses – it cannot be seen, heard, smelt or tasted – it quite naturally arouses irrational rather than rational fear. Supporters of the industry make the point that radiation, which has been with us since the dawn of life, is 'natural' and therefore should not give rise to fear. 'Radiation, at least at the levels man is likely to meet in his natural environment, represents no significant hazard, compared to the many others that man meets in nature.' So says nuclear worker and author Ian Blair. These natural sources are cosmic (from space), trace elements (in rocks and soil), radon gas (a radioactive decay product of uranium), and that given off from the human body by radioactive elements (chiefly potassium-40 in the blood stream).

Some radioactive materials remain active for thousands of years, a potential danger to future generations. For example, the radioactive plutonium created now will still be emitting radiation in the year AD 24,000, although the amount of plutonium will have reduced to half today's level. Human beings exposed to radioactive material may not experience health problems at once: these may only surface after 10 or 20 years or even longer.

Radioactivity is associated with the nuclear power cycle in the following ways:

(i) the preparation of uranium and uranium fuels for the reactor

(ii) the fuel content of the reactor, if breached, may spread radioactivity

(iii) the waste discharged from the reactors may be radioactive

(iv) the structure of and equipment in the reactors itself becomes radioactive

(v) fuel removed from the reactor, or spent fuel, is highly radioactive.

Radiation doses are measured in sieverts and millisieverts (mSv), the latter being one thousandth of a sievert. The natural sources mentioned above are estimated to give each human being an average total dose of 2.2 mSv a year. But this depends where we live. The average dose in Cornwall is 6.3 mSv, mainly from radon gas, and in some areas of Brazil and India there is 20 times as much background radiation.

There are of course other man-made sources of radiation besides nuclear power, the best known being X-rays. In 1928 an international body – the International Commission on Radiological Protection (ICRP) – was set up to

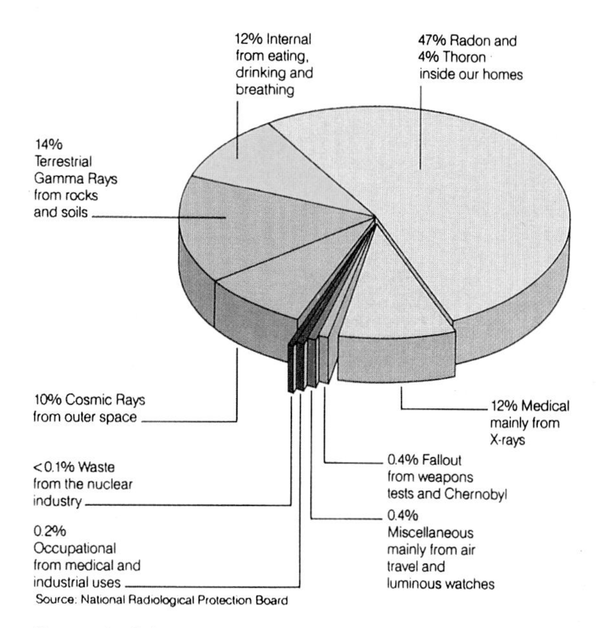


Sources of radiation exposure for the UK population

decide limits on radiation exposure for people working with such radioactive materials. By 1951, the UK Whole Body dose limit for occupationally exposed workers was equivalent to 250 mSv/year. The limit was progressively reduced over the years until by 1977 it stood at 50 mSv. In 1987, Britain's National Radiological Protection Board recommended that the annual limit be further reduced to 15 mSv/year. Similar proposals were also put forward by the Health and Safety Executive in 1990.

According to the HSE, out of a total of some 600,000 radiation workers, only about a third of one per cent (about 2000 employees) actually receive an annual dose of 15 mSv or above in any one year. For the general public, the radiation dose limit is 1 mSv per year from man-made sources excluding medical exposure, although radiation doses up to 5 mSv are permissible in some years, provided that the total radiation dose over a lifetime does not exceed 70 mSv. The average dose to the UK population from the nuclear industry is less than 0.01 mSv per year or less than 0.1% of the individual's total radiation dose from natural and man-made sources.

The general public did not, until recent years, show much concern about radiation effects from the power industry; its main fears were focused on the dangers of nuclear war and the increase in the number of nuclear weapon accidents over the years. There were an estimated 63 serious accidents of the latter kind between 1950 and 1973, only four of which were attributed to the Russians or Chinese. Publicity about such accidents has been minimal; gradually the general public took the view that it was improbable that a bomb would ever detonate by accident. Fear that this might happen has now taken second place to concern about an accident at a nuclear power station.

Supporters of the nuclear power industry stress the difference between a bomb and a power station. 'One thing cannot happen to a nuclear reactor,' says Blair. 'It cannot explode like an atomic bomb. The reason for this is very simple. In order to get a nuclear explosion, one needs more than a critical mass of fissile material at high concentrations.' There is a large mass of fissile material in the core of a reactor, but the concentration even in enriched fuel is only 2 or 3 per cent – 'nowhere near enough to cause a nuclear explosion,' says Blair. Others disagree and describe Chernobyl as, in any practical sense, an explosion.

Other experts in the nuclear field use the word 'explosion' to describe what could happen if a nuclear power plant should suffer an accident, or an incident leading to a meltdown. Such a meltdown could occur because of the failure to take heat away from the reactor core,

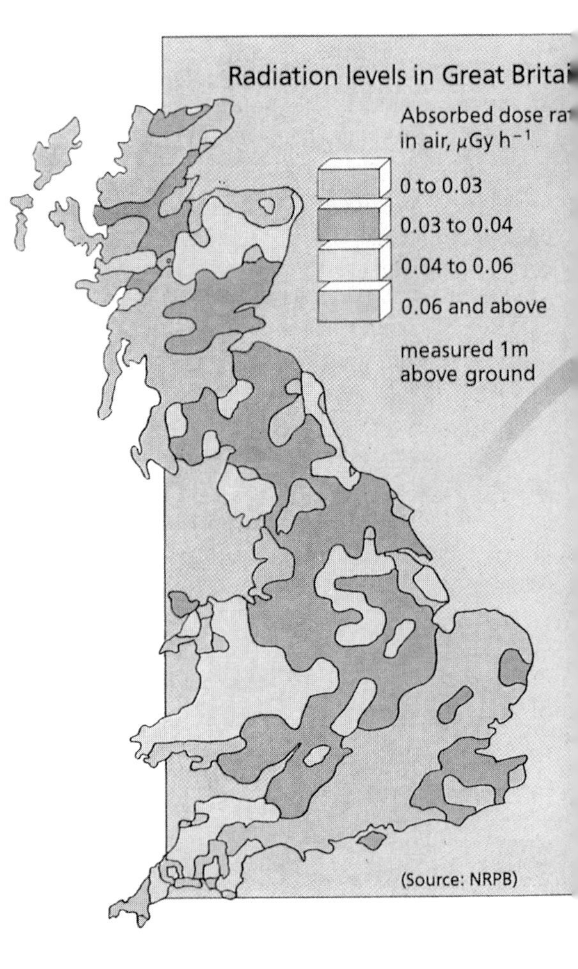


a fracture of its protective shield, and a resultant release of radioactivity into the atmosphere. Release of radioactivity is the main danger in a nuclear accident. After Chernobyl it is not surprising that many people still believe that a radiation release, which then spreads over hundreds of miles, begins with an 'explosion'. Such fears can be exacerbated by calculations such as those made by a physicist at the University of California, who concluded somewhat emotively that 'each large reactor of 1000 megawatt capacity contains as much radioactivity as would be released if one hundred thousand Hiroshima bombs were simultaneously exploded.'

Before Chernobyl, while there had been accidents in nuclear power stations, there had never been one in which radiation had caused proven public loss of life. (There had been accidents in nuclear *research* plants which had resulted in the deaths of workers.) This enabled the British nuclear industry to say, with perfect truth, that there was no evidence of any injury, lethal or otherwise, to any member of the public or to a worker employed in a nuclear power station here. The annual average dose of radiation from nuclear power stations received by the general public can, as already noted, be described as negligible, and the radiation dose affecting some workers, while criticised by some authorities, is not accepted by the industry as a cause of injury.

Chernobyl has destroyed public confidence that a nuclear accident resulting in deaths from radiation is statistically unlikely, even if this remains true. According to 1988 reports from Russia, about 300 people living in the vicinity of the power station suffered from radiation sickness after the accident. Of these, 33 died. Nikolai Bochkov, director of the Moscow Institute of Medical Genetics, says that more than 2,000 people in the Soviet Union will die over the next 20 years owing to cancer induced by radiation from Chernobyl. In addition 200 children will suffer from diseases inherited from their parents. British estimates put the increase in deaths from cancer, outside Russia, as a result of Chernobyl, at 2040. Adding these figures together, estimates of eventual cancer deaths from Chernobyl total 4073. Some other estimates are lower and the comparison has to be made with millions of 'natural' cancer deaths. The facts of the case remain elusive. In mid-1990, the Russian authorities announced the proposed evacuation of 14,000 more people from the Chernobyl area.

Before Chernobyl, many experts on nuclear affairs calculated the risk of an accident of this type, resulting in deaths outside the confines of the station itself, to be very small. The implication was that nuclear power stations were statistically absolutely safe. For example, Sir Alan Cottrell, formerly Chief Scientific Adviser to the British government, in what was described as 'a totally objective book', considered that the risk of deaths from a reactor accident amounted to one tenth of the risk that the same number of people would be killed on the ground by falling aircraft. Taking the latter as an unlikely – and therefore acceptable – risk, he pointed out that 'a catastrophic nuclear accident which caused the deaths of over 1,000 people would occur once in about 10,000 years on this basis.' Similarly a single death might occur about once in ten years. This calculation assumed the existence

Chernobyl: the melt-down that had a huge impact on public opinion.

of 1000 similar reactors throughout the world. Unfortunately for this comparison, a spate of aircraft accidents has made the public uneasy about deaths from this cause too and Cottrell's statistical 'risk' figures are less soothing.

Chernobyl brought any such estimates rather closer to home. Sir Alan quoted F. R. Farmer of the UKAEA as having estimated that the amount of radiation emitted in the event of an accident causing 1,000 deaths (bearing in mind the uncertainty of wind speed and direction, and the siting of the reactor), would be approximately ten million curies (370,000 TBq). A single reactor, he said, would be likely to release ten million curies less than once in ten million years. At the time he was writing, Sir Alan admitted that it was impossible to check the performance of the nuclear power industry because 'there have been no public casualties from nuclear accidents and so no accident statistics.' Now Chernobyl has provided the statistics.

Since Chernobyl, the nuclear industry has in general used an argument which can be summarised briefly under the title 'Why it couldn't happen here.' The CEGB, for example, explained that the Chernobyl reactor is of a type 'not in use anywhere else in the world'.

> Investigations into the cause of the accident showed that [this type of reactor] the RBMK had serious design faults which would not be allowed in any reactor built in Britain. The Russians were aware of the faults and relied on operating instructions to overcome them. Yet at Chernobyl operators ignored these instructions.

Lord Marshall also described Chernobyl as 'a hybrid . . . a chimera'.

The Greens reacted by retorting that not only were Hanford reactors in Washington State, USA, very similar in design, but the early British Magnox reactors of Calder Hall and Chapelcross also, like Chernobyl, had

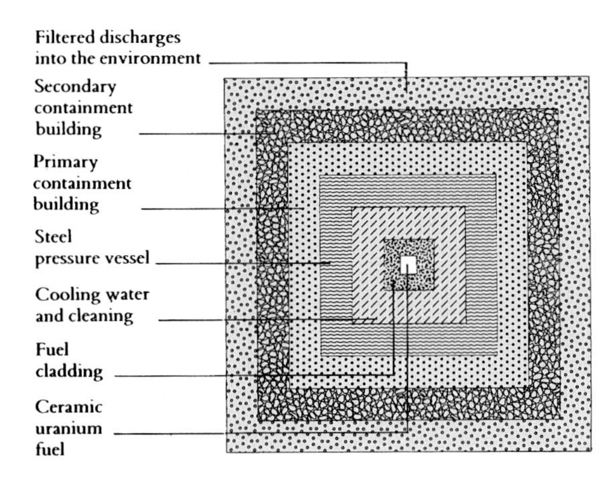


The nuclear industry, which states that Chernobyl 'could not happen here' backs its assertion with diagrams like this showing that the design of the PWR's basic systems ensures the effectiveness of the safety barriers at all times.

inadequate containment. They drew a detailed comparison between the Russian designs for containment and those in other countries round the world, concluding that 'a Chernobyl-type accident may be far less unlikely than hitherto accepted.'

There is no need to study in detail here the various nuclear reactor accidents over the past thirty years; readers who wish to do so will find information in many books published before Chernobyl, such as those written by Walter C. Patterson and Jim Garrison. Here, we concentrate upon three or four of the most significant.

One of the first accidents occurred in Britain at the military reactor at Windscale (Sellafield) in 1957. Blair describes this reactor as a very crude device by comparison with a modern commercial installation. The accident occurred when, as a result of inadequate plant instrumentation, the physicist in charge of a plutonium-producing reactor threw a switch too soon while following a routine operation. It was nearly two days before there was a sign

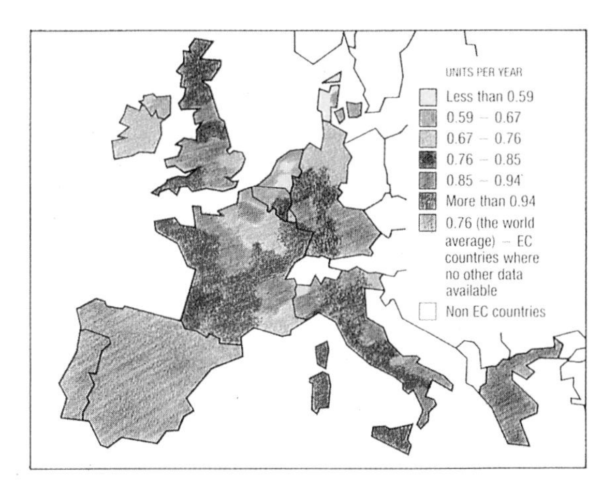


Variations in annual radiation dose from cosmic rays, ground and buildings in European Community countries.

that anything was wrong, and a further 24 hours before the resulting fire was controlled by water hoses. Hazardous radioactivity, however, had escaped over Cumberland: amongst other precautions, some two million litres of milk was poured into rivers and the sea. Information about this accident released in 1989 has exacerbated rather than reduced public concern about the long-term effects.

Five years before the Windscale fire, there had been an accident at the NRX research reactor in Chalk River, 200 km north of Ottawa, Canada, again as the result of human error. A technician opened some valves by mistake and his supervisor, realising what had happened, reset the valves, but telephoned incorrect remedial instructions to his assistant. A safety device which should have corrected the problem failed to operate. Within seventy seconds, radioactivity alarms were sounding. The fission energy did not produce an explosion, but the resultant gases did, and the reactor core was effectively demolished. The emergency procedures at the plant were effective: official reports maintained that none of the staff suffered excessive radiation exposure either then or during the year-long clean-up.

In Switzerland, the Lucens reactor, built in a cavern under a hill, released radioactive coolant and heavy water into the containment when it was restarted in 1969, after being shut down for about two months for routine maintenance. Fortunately, air locks automatically sealed the cavern and there was nobody on the wrong side. The accident had been caused by the failure of a pressure tube, not by operator error. It took over two years to decontaminate and dismantle the plant, after which it was decided to use the cavern for storing radioactive waste.

The first major reactor accident in the USA, in 1961, was at the prototype military reactor plant SL-1 in Idaho. For reasons that will remain unknown (Patterson suggests thoughtlessness – horseplay perhaps), a

Windscale *c.*1957, where one of the first nuclear accidents occurred.

central control rod was pulled out of the core by one of the three young servicemen on duty. All three were killed. It was months before the level of radiation fell low enough to permit an investigation.

A far more serious accident occurred at the Enrico Fermi fast-breeder reactor, south of Detroit, which suffered a melt-down, owing to the failure of a safety device which had been insecurely anchored during construction. Fortunately the core stopped short of complete melt-down, otherwise the outcome might have been what someone sardonically called the 'China Syndrome'. This means, in Patterson's words, that 'the molten mass of highly reactive fuel, generating its own fierce heat and far beyond any hope of cooling or control, might sear its way through all the containments and into the rock below the foundations of the reactor, melting, burning and exploding as it went', bound for the opposite pole of the earth, in that case China, or, from Britain, down to Australia.

Thus by the end of the 1960s there had been major accidents in Canada, Britain, the United States and Switzerland – major in the sense that in each case there was a potential risk of exposing the public to radiation, although, so far as is known, this did not happen. The public responded by beginning to show some disquiet, particularly about the safety record of the plants protected by a light-water shield, the PWR and BWR. This was at a time when the American-designed light-water reactor was overtaking the different designs pioneered by Britain, Canada and others.

There has not been a major accident at a PWR, but there have been what Patterson describes as 'some near misses'. For example, there was the now well-known incident in March 1975 at Browns Ferry station in Alabama, at that time the world's largest nuclear power station in operation. An electrician and his mate were using a lighted candle to check the airflow through holes made in the walls for cables. A draught caught the flame and ignited the foam plastic packing around a cable tray – and the fire spread to the reactor building before the electrician could put it out. The fire burned for several hours, but there was no radioactivity release, although Browns Ferry was out of action for 18 months.

Perhaps the most notorious near miss of all took place in the new nuclear plant on an island in the Shenandoah River near Harrisburg, Pennsylvania, in March 1979. This was Three Mile Island. The initial cause was the failure of several feed-water pumps. Neither of the two operators in the control room noticed this, despite panel warning lights. According to Patterson 'what followed, for the next three days, was an almost unbelievable chronicle of confusion, misinformation, contradictory advice and – for the hapless thousands of people living in south-west Pennsylvania – nightmare uncertainty.' There was a hydrogen explosion inside the reactor, and although there was little release of radioactivity – because of the design of the reactor – the Government of Pennsylvania, in the absence of any positive responses from the experts, recommended that children and pregnant women within a five-mile radius be evacuated. Many people further away also left home.

No one was killed or even injured at Three Mile Island but, in the eyes of some commentators, its effects were profound. According to Blair, since nothing actually happened this 'tended to lead to a sense of anticlimax.' He suggests that it was not a 'near miss' but 'a very serious accident indeed': the effects were minimal, he says, not because of good luck, but because 'nuclear power stations are designed with multiple containment systems.' On the other hand, Patterson notes that a report chaired by Michael Rogorin of the NRC found that the reactor was within sixty minutes of melt-down and that 'a catastrophe had been avoided mainly by dumb luck' (or 'pure luck' as we would say). Patterson says the accident 'shook nuclear policy to its foundations. Its impact outside the USA was almost as dramatic as its impact within.' According to him, it changed nuclear policy in Germany and Sweden – as well as resulting in a virtual cessation of nuclear development in the United States.

The much more serious accident at Chernobyl was, according to British experts, also the result of a design defect, this time triggered off by an improperly authorised experiment. Excess steam blew off the reactor roof. There was no nuclear explosion 'in the sense of an atomic bomb', but there was a rapid build-up of power leading to a pressure surge and a steam and hydrogen explosion. An explosion which causes a widespread release of radioactivity, even if not a nuclear 'explosion', has much the same effect on public perceptions.

It has already been noted that British nuclear power authorities believe Chernobyl could not happen here. However the number of operator errors in previous accidents is advanced by critics as an indication that 'breaking the rules' is a possibility anywhere in the world. This same point is made about safety features which, critics point out, have failed in the past. Supporters of nuclear power respond that 'the really big disaster will not happen because it cannot happen . . . the designs they have chosen are *intrinsically* safe. Chernobyl happened because the RMBK reactor was not intrinsically safe.'

Intended as the definitive account of the Chernobyl disaster, the Watt Committee report of 1988 concluded that while no inherent weaknesses in design could be identified in UK plants, nor in qualifications of their staff or the safety inspectorate, it was harder to assess whether 'organisational or structural [administrative] weaknesses' could result in a similar accident here.

One area of concern was the staffing levels of the Nuclear Installations Inspectorate.

The CEGB admitted after Chernobyl that 'it is probable that lessons can be learnt about emergency planning procedures.' At present these procedures, to come into effect if there were an accident in the United Kingdom, are reviewed once a year by the Nuclear Installations Inspectorate, the body set up by the government in 1959 to oversee the safety of all nuclear plants. In 1988, after the Government issued its own White Paper *Chernobyl: the Government's Reaction,* the House of Commons Select Committee on Agriculture reviewed it and came to the

Three Mile Island, the scene of the most publicised of nuclear accidents – until Chernobyl.

Collecting grass samples for analysis, near BNFL's Capenhurst works, Chester. The objective is to submit the samples for radiation analysis.

Collecting seaweed for analysis, near Chapelcross power station, Dumfriesshire, Scotland. There are four nuclear reactors at Chapelcross.

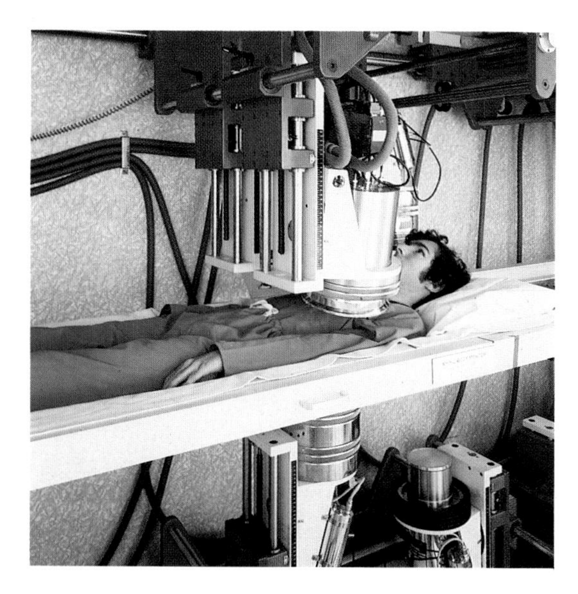

In the safety services department at Sellafield, all employees undergo regular health checks. This man is being monitored for plutonium in the chest.

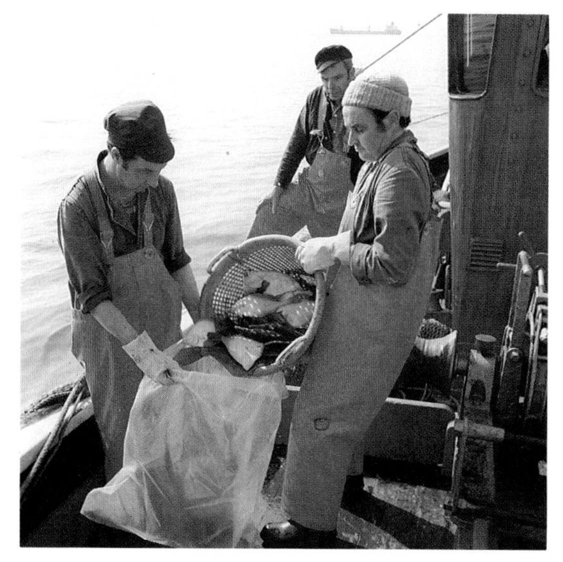

Monitoring radiation levels off Saltmarsh near the Sellafield site, in Cumbria. Critics claim that excessive levels have been found, but BNFL disputes this.

conclusion that, in effect, there were no national contingency plans for a Chernobyl-type disaster, and regional plans were inadequate.

Earlier in this chapter, details were given about the levels of radiation which were 'acceptable' for workers in the industry. The government also set such levels for the population at large and these were discussed in a general way in their White Paper on Chernobyl. Not all the critics agree with the levels calculated. For example Professor J. Rotblat, Emeritus Professor of Physics in the University of London and formerly of St Bartholomew's Hospital Medical School, said, as long ago as the mid 1970s: 'I myself am not happy about present (permitted) levels of radiation. I feel they ought to be lowered.'

What happens if there is an accident and people or their property are exposed to radiation? In America, no sooner had the potential results of nuclear accidents been publicly investigated than the insurance companies refused to give cover to the private companies building the reactors. (In America, power supplies are mostly controlled by the private utility companies, not nationalised or state-controlled organisations.) As a result, the Eisenhower Administration persuaded Congress to pass the Price-Anderson Act as an amendment to the Atomic Energy Act, setting an upper limit to what the utilities would have to pay to injured parties. In the United Kingdom, similarly, the limit as to what would be paid in third-party liability was restricted by Act of Parliament. Following Chernobyl, farmers in Scotland, Cumbria and Wales submitted claims for damages because of the cost of keeping sheep after the radioactive cloud passed over their farms in May 1986. Compensation payments to these farmers exceeded £5.5 million at January 1990.

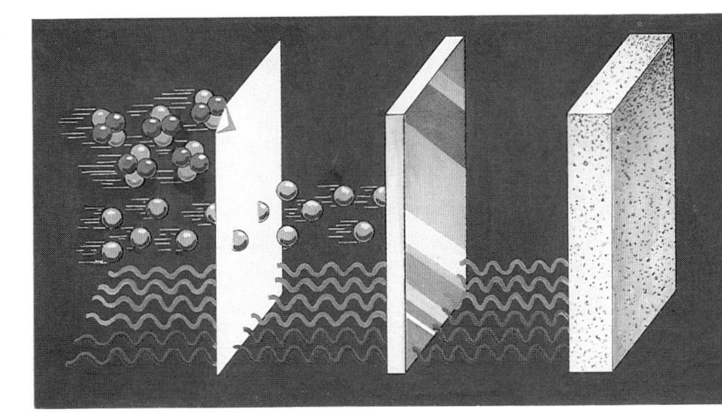

Different types of shielding are required for protection against the various rays emitted by uranium. Alpha rays, the least penetrating, can be stopped by paper. Beta rays require 6 mm aluminium and Gamma rays thick concrete.

Whether the Government will apply to the Russians for matching compensation is not known.

Parents of young people living near Sellafield who have developed leukaemia are suing its owners, BNFL, claiming that Sellafield operations have raised the risk of leukaemia in the area around the plant. In order to succeed in their claim, the parents would have to prove that on the balance of probability, the individual case of leukaemia was caused by the operation of the Sellafield nuclear plant. BNFL contests the claim, saying that there is no direct evidence of a causal link, and it has support from other authorities, notably the National Radiological Protection Board, who have continually updated and assessed the risk of radiation-induced leukaemia.

The Black Enquiry was set up following a Yorkshire Television programme in 1983 entitled *Windscale: the Nuclear Laundry.* Under the chairmanship of Sir Douglas Black, it studied available evidence about geographical patterns of cancer, particularly around Sellafield. Black stated that while the incidence of leukaemia was high in the nearby village of

Seascale, the link with the nuclear installation was not proven. In some quarters, Black's conclusion was regarded as a whitewash, but a paper by two experts who stress that 'we are connected with neither the nuclear industry nor anti-nuclear organisations' strongly suggests that Black's conclusions are reasonable. On the other hand, they recommend that – instead of reiterating that no proven health links exist, and that if they do they may not be evident for 50 years – the nuclear industry should

(a) minimise public exposure to radiation, in case expert opinion is wrong
(b) help to establish an extensive and accurate public dose-monitoring system
(c) fund basic research into low-level radiation effects.

Since they wrote this an industry-funded research project has been started.

Early in 1990, a further study was published (known as the Gardner report), which suggested that there could be an association between exposure to radiation of Sellafield employees and leukaemia in their children. The report concluded that other factors such as spending time on the beach, eating fish from the Irish Sea or X-rays of mothers during pregnancy could not explain the excess of leukaemias in West Cumbria. In contrast, for children of fathers working at Sellafield at the time of their conception, the risk of developing leukaemia was found to be about 2.5 times greater. The same degree of risk was also found to apply to children with fathers working in the iron and steel and chemical industries and in agriculture. Where the father's radiation dose was 100 mSv or more, the risk factor was over six times greater. BNFL has pointed out that the conclusion was based on only 10 such cases over a period of 36 years, but nevertheless BNFL has said that the report causes concern and has called for further research. They stress that while a continuing programme to reduce exposure at Sellafield has already cut doses to about one quarter of the levels experienced 20 years ago, the company is urgently investigating what action needs to be taken to reduce radiation exposure of its employees even further.

| *Cause of Death* | *Total Deaths* | *Number of deaths per millions of population** |
|---|---|---|
| All deaths | 590,734 | 11,832.8 |
| Road traffic accidents | 4,832 | 96.8 |
| Suicide | 4,419 | 88.5 |
| Accidental falls | 3,907 | 78.3 |
| Drowning and suffocation | 843 | 16.9 |
| Fire and flames | 649 | 13.0 |
| Accidental poisoning | 598 | 12.0 |
| Accidents - natural factors | 456 | 9.1 |
| Homicide | 344 | 6.9 |
| Medical procedures | 155 | 3.1 |
| Railway accidents | 91 | 1.8 |
| Water transport accidents | 60 | 1.2 |
| Air transport accidents | 45 | 0.9 |
| Radiation accidents | 0 | 0 |

** 1985 population of England and Wales taken as 49,923,500*

The numbers of deaths from various causes are shown in the above table. The figures are taken from the report of the Office of Population Censuses and Surveys for England and Wales for 1985. Since no proven deaths have been caused to the population at large from nuclear radiation, such comparisons are used to show the relative safety of nuclear power – but they have their limitations.

This chapter has been primarily concerned with the effects of a major accident in a nuclear power station. The Sellafield controversy relates to the effects, if any, of leakages from a reprocessing plant, rather than an accident or incident at a power station. The industry points out that during the 26 years that commercial reactors have been in operation, there is no evidence that any harm has been caused by

Various organisations have statutory responsibility for the safety of nuclear installations – most of them national, but some international. In brief these are as follows:

| Organisation | Responsibility |
| --- | --- |
| Nuclear Electric | safety of its installations |
| Nuclear Installations Inspectorate | licensing – design, construction and operation |
| National Radiological Protection Board | advice on radiological protection |
| International Commission on Radiological Protection | recommendations on exposure of workers and public to radiation |
| International Atomic Energy Agency | regulations covering transport of irradiated fuel |
| Department of the Environment Ministry of Agriculture, Fisheries and Food | authorisation of radioactive discharges |
| Department of Transport | approved transport of irradiated material |

radiation to any member of the public. They admit that 'there is a small increase in radiation near a nuclear power station [but] it has a negligible effect on the local community.' Critics, particularly those living locally, do not necessarily agree. Curiously enough, the British public itself appears to be more concerned about the effects of the problems arising from reprocessing nuclear fuel and waste management generally than they do about the possibility of another Chernobyl.

The next chapter will concentrate on the debate about the waste, which results mainly from the reprocessing of spent fuel from power stations.

# 7. WASTE

Scientists have identified 6000 pieces of waste space industry debris floating in outer space and have calculated that a further one million pieces less than 1 centimetre in diameter are out there too. Any one of these, even as small as a fleck of paint, could damage other objects in space like spacecraft, missiles or aeroplanes, possibly with disastrous results for those of us back on earth. The word 'waste' seems a rather inadequate description for such potentially dangerous material, and so it does for many other by-products of industrial activity which are potentially harmful to human beings, particularly material which is also radioactive.

Research shows that the British public believes that the radioactive waste produced by nuclear power industry is the most cogent reason for objecting to the latter's continued growth. Worries about an environmental disaster of some kind, perhaps arising from the spread of nuclear waste, have overtaken fear of nuclear war.

The industry, in contrast, believes that public fears are ill-founded and that nuclear waste can be disposed of or stored with complete safety. It believes that it has the technology, and has only been held back by lack of political will to take the practical steps necessary. If in the past the industry could be accused of a lack of openness on the subject of waste, in the last few years it has positively encouraged widespread discussion of the issues involved. In the short term, such openness does not always allay fear, but in the longer term it must be of help in developing understanding of the issues on both sides.

In 1986, the House of Commons Select Committee on the Environment, under the chairmanship of Sir Hugh Rossi, produced a report which was highly critical about the then state of information about nuclear waste:

> The UK government and nuclear industry are confused. . . . A very large proportion of radioactive waste goes on being produced unquestioned and . . . the UK is still only feeling its way towards a coherent policy. . . . This is regrettably inadequate.

How big a problem is it? In one sense, it is relatively small. Over 5 million tonnes of general toxic (i.e. harmful to humans) waste has to be disposed of every year in Britain from licensed sites. Responsibility for its disposal rests with whichever industry is producing it; responsibility for 'policing' its safety by licensing and regulation lies with the Department of the Environment's new Pollution Inspectorate. As the diagram on pp. 66-7 shows, radioactive waste from nuclear power stations is only a tiny fraction of the total of 5 million plus tonnes of toxic waste – something like 11,000 tonnes in total.

But size is not the point. Depending on the type of radioactive material, quite small amounts of nuclear waste can remain radioactive, and possibly hazardous, for very long periods of time, although others will decay away to form inert material quite quickly. It should be noted that in other types of toxic waste the toxicity never diminishes. Sir Alan Cottrell, in his book *How Safe is Nuclear Energy?*, gives the following explanation for the long life of some radioactive materials:

> A nucleus can become unstable in several different ways. One of the simplest is that it may have excessive energy, so that its protons and neutrons move about energetically inside the nucleus, jostling each other and vibrating vigorously. In this case, the particles may relapse into a calmer state of motion by expelling their surplus energy out of the nucleus in the form of a *gamma ray.* A gamma ray is a unit pulse of pure radiation . . . .
> Nuclei can also be unstable because they contain the 'wrong' numbers of protons and neutrons . . . [and] often *transmute* into different nuclei, with better numbers, by *radioactivity,* emitting nuclear particles. They may in this way disintegrate either of their own accord or when stimulated to do so by a visiting nuclear particle. There are two common types of disintegration . . . an *alpha* particle [and] a *beta* particle.

Having described how nuclei can become unstable and decompose, Sir Alan goes on:

> No one can say when a given unstable nucleus will disintegrate spontaneously. There is no warning and no fixed lifetime before it happens. It occurs suddenly, out of the blue; a single sharp event that seems to happen purely by chance. The only regular feature is the *half-life* of a large number of such nuclei. This means that, if we start off today with, say, one million radium atoms, then in 1600 years' time there could still be about 500,000 of these as yet undecomposed. After a second 1600 years, about 250,000 radium atoms would still be left. After a third 1600 years, the number would have dropped to about 125,000 and so on. During each 1600 years about half the nuclei 'die' but those that happen not to die remain, as it were, completely 'ageless' until they in turn chance to die. Very broadly . . . nuclei with half-lives on a timescale familiar to human beings – say from a few minutes to several years – are the most dangerous to health.

Thus the high-level waste produced in the course of the nuclear power cycle is potentially dangerous because of the radiation it emits, and because it may remain radioactive for a very long period of time: after suitable treatment and storage, it will only be disposed of when it is 'safe'. The problems of storage in the meantime are considerable.

The nuclear industry believes these problems are being solved, and have built a new plant to treat the high-level waste by turning it into a solid suitable for eventual disposal. Critics believe that the disposal problems are intractable and, in the words of Miss J. M. Pick who wrote to *The Times* on 15 November 1988, that 'the only really safe and economical way to deal with nuclear waste . . . is not to create it in the first place.' Even if this comment were valid, there would still be the existing waste to deal with. And even if Britain itself ceased to use nuclear power, there would

The proportion (by weight) of reprocessing products at Sellafield. Although less than 3 per cent are classified as highly active waste, critics would argue that it is not its weight but its radioactivity which is the problem.

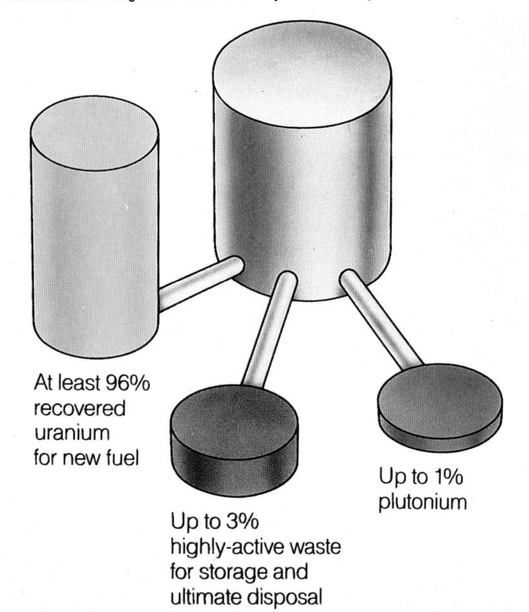

Used nuclear fuel, transported in massive flasks, arrive at Sellafield to be stored and decanned before being reprocessed. Sellafield in West Cumbria is the site where BNFL deals with the full range of radioactive wastes – the majority of which arise from the company's reprocessing activities. In simple terms, reprocessing involves the recovery of valuable uranium and plutonium from nuclear fuel which has been used to generate electricity.

be other nations doing so and manufacturing waste. The problem is therefore international and continuing.

Critics who take an international view of the nuclear industry often say that its supporters are acting immorally by producing long-life radioactive waste which could be a hazard to future generations, centuries after those who produced it are dead. Such criticism might well be applied to the human race in general, which does not take a highly moral view of its responsibilities towards posterity. It greedily uses up the earth's natural resources like oil and coal, spreads toxic poisons over farmlands, puffs harmful gases into the atmosphere, disfigures the countryside with coal slag heaps and generally plays mayhem with its inheritance. Such irresponsibility does not, however, free us from answering the specific question 'Will future generations be burdened with a serious radioactivity problem owing to present-day nuclear power stations?'

Sir Alan Cottrell believes they will not. He points out that the millions of tonnes of uranium occurring naturally in the earth have an extremely long half-life (4500 million years). As this uranium slowly decays into radium, radon, etc, life on the planet is exposed to the most damaging form of radiation, alpha particles. Today, for the first time in history, man is taking small amounts from the earth's stock of uranium and, by using them in nuclear reactors, making them disintegrate much more quickly than if they were left in the earth. 'For each uranium atom which disappears through fission (in nuclear power plants) a few new radioactive atoms, mainly of the beta and gamma-emitting kind appear. Most of these new atoms quickly disintegrate inside the reactor, and about 90 per cent of the remainder do so' (when the fuel rods are stored after being removed from it). The net result, therefore, says Sir Alan, is a small reduction in the number of radioactive atoms. But what matters is not the number of atoms, but their radioactivity, which depends on half-lives as well as numbers. 'Even here, if we take a sufficiently long view, the result of man's efforts is to reduce the world's radioactivity slightly, because we are consuming some uranium atoms and replacing them with radioactive products which mostly have shorter half-lives and so decay more quickly.'

Sir Alan concludes: 'On a really long time scale, then, there is no moral case against us.' This may be so, but he admits that this decrease in the earth's radioactivity is 'gained at the expense of a short-term increase'.

The short-term position is that 'waste'

nuclear fuel rods, freshly withdrawn from an active reactor when they are 'spent', have a radioactivity about a million times greater than the ore mined from the earth. After the first year in the cooling ponds, their radioactivity has dropped to being about 10,000 times as active as the ore, weight for weight. When most of the uranium and plutonium has been removed in the reprocessing plant, the remaining waste takes about 10 years to drop to about 1000 times the activity of the ore; after 1000 years, the radiation drops to about the same level as in the natural ore from which the rods were made.

There are, therefore, several hundred years in which to be concerned about the radioactivity of the highly active wastes resulting from nuclear power. It is also necessary to be concerned about the less active wastes: these will be considered in the following chapter.

'High-level' waste is a name for certain kinds of waste which the Department of the Environment describes in layman's terms as those 'in which temperatures may rise significantly as a result of their radioactivity.' It is of course the most dangerous category of nuclear waste. The industry and the government persistently emphasise that the quantities involved are small, as the greater part of the spent fuel can be used again after reprocessing.

The nuclear industry stresses that, compared with other energy producers, nuclear power results in significantly smaller amounts of waste. BNFL points out that a large coal-fired power station emits yearly some 10 million tonnes of carbon dioxide and 200,000 tonnes of sulphur dioxide and nitrous oxide. In addition, a million tonnes of coal ash is produced, of which about 4,000 tonnes is emitted up the chimney. BNFL illustrates the

This spent nuclear fuel arrives at Sellafield contained in specially designed transport flasks up to 110 tonnes in weight and constructed from thick steel and lead. They are lifted by giant handling equipment.

Spent fuel is stored underwater at Sellafield.

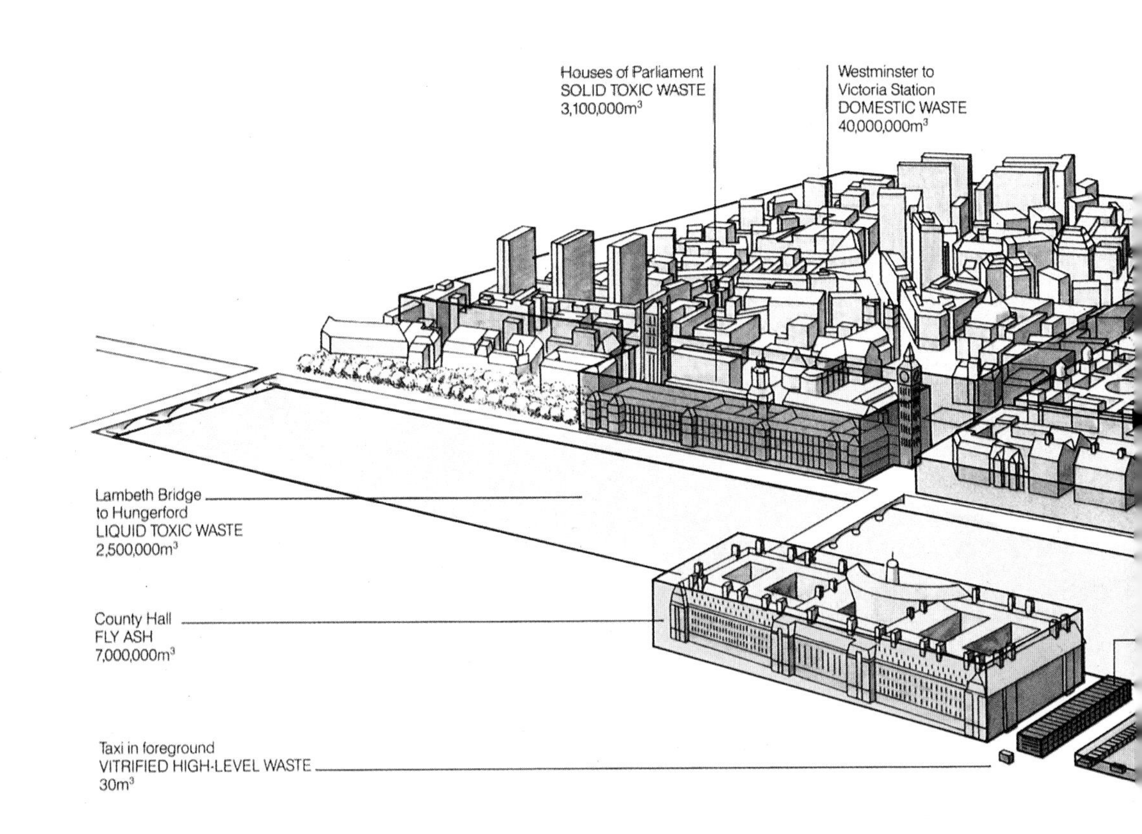


The total volumes of waste produced annually in the UK, represented as proportions of Central London. This diagram is used by the nuclear industry to indicate the relatively small scale of the high-level waste problem.

point by a diagram (originating from the Department of the Environment) which shows the total volume of waste produced annually in the United Kingdom, represented as proportions of central London. Vitrified high-level waste from the nuclear industry is shown as the size of a mere taxi. Intermediate nuclear waste is a modest-sized building and low-level waste covers a car park.

Critics of the nuclear programme concentrate their attack on other aspects of nuclear waste. Walter Patterson gives a vivid picture of what this small quantity of radioactively dangerous waste looks like.

> When a fresh fuel element enters a reactor it is as sleek and glossy as a surgical implant. When it emerges after radiation it is discoloured, possibly even swollen, caked with what the nuclear engineers call crud.

A similarly emotive description might well be given of the waste which results from coal production. Indeed coal wastes have been described as 'very dangerous, and, unlike the nuclear wastes, many of them remain dangerous for ever.'

Spent nuclear fuel rods from UK stations are

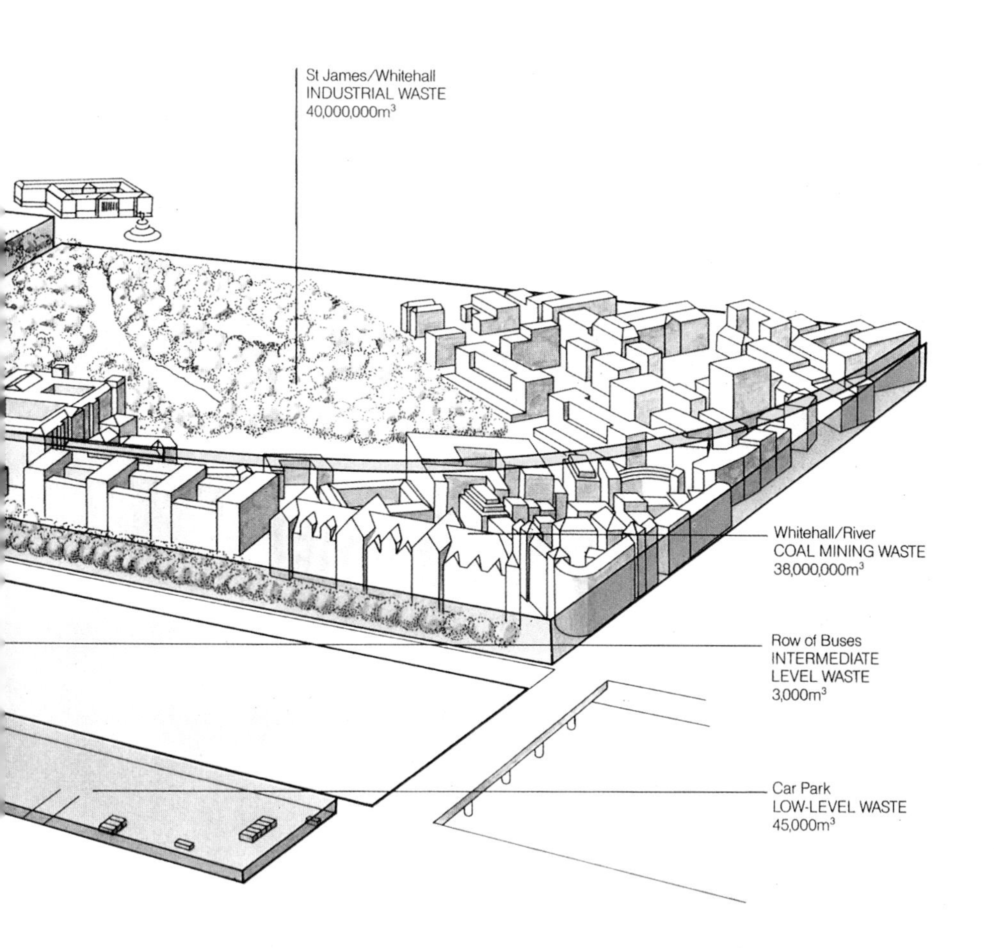


normally reprocessed at BNFL's plant at Sellafield. There, after mechanical treatment, the rods are immersed in an acid solution and the high-level liquid waste which results is stored in stainless steel tanks – as it has been for more than 30 years. The waste is at most 3 per cent of the original volume of the spent fuel rods and this can be kept in 21 large specially-designed tanks at Sellafield (for Magnox rods the waste is only 0.5 per cent). These tanks are all double contained, with seven separate cooling circuits. However, it is generally accepted that storage in solid form has great advantages over liquid storage – it reduces the possibility of an escape of radioactivity, is easier to supervise and transport and hence more economical to send for disposal. The liquid wastes, instead of being stored in tanks, will be incorporated by BNFL in borosilicate glass blocks – vitrification – and sealed inside stainless steel containers, thus becoming 'solid'.

In 1990 a new vitrification plant (based on a French vitrification process) was in full operation at Sellafield. BNFL's plan is that the containers of vitrified waste will be held in a

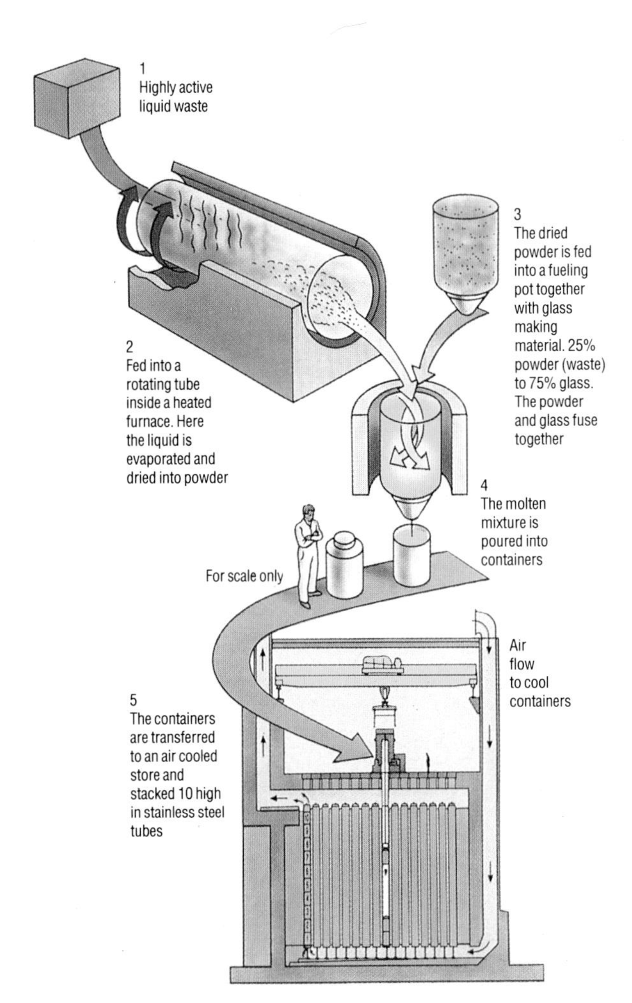


The vitrification process to convert highly active liquid waste into glass blocks.

natural convection air-cooled store for at least 50 years, by which time the heat generation will have reduced to a point when 'disposal' can be arranged. A year's high-level waste from a 1000 MW nuclear station could be stored in about 30 containers, each about the height and diameter of a milk churn.

Much emphasis is placed on the small volume of this high-level waste in the UK. But it has to be remembered that similar storage installations are located in the USA, France, the Soviet Union, and elsewhere. In addition, there is a large (but unquantifiable) volume of waste from the military programmes designed to recover plutonium. The largest of these, so far as is known, is in Washington State, USA, where 151 large tanks contain nearly 250,000 cubic metres. The total amount of high-level waste in the world as a whole is therefore substantial and growing.

The waste containers will be stored in air-cooled chambers at the Sellafield reprocessing plant for at least 50 years. Few of those initially responsible for production of the waste will thus be still doing their jobs when the time comes to move it on: the decision as to how and where to dispose of it will have to be taken by succeeding generations. No one knows now what they will decide, although experts hold various views about their preferred solution. Sir Alan Cottrell, for example, proposes to keep them 'permanently immured in deep vaults about half a mile below ground. The access tunnels to these vaults would eventually be filled in with rocks and earth.' At such a depth, the earth's crust is inactive and 'the geological structures and materials down there remain stable for millions of years,' says Sir Alan, noting however that 'the only major geological event which might occur in the near future is another ice age.' 'Experience of past ice ages,' he reports comfortingly, 'show that glaciers do not, on average, scrape away the surface of the land to a depth below about one quarter of a mile.' He concludes: 'The preferred places for the burial of the cylinders – a few thousand in each vault, spaced out to allow each to be separately cooled by its surrounding material – are in geologically dry deposits of granite, in thick salt beds or in clay-rich rocks.'

Sir Alan points out that the main danger is that radioactive substances might somehow become dissolved in water which would eventually find its way to the surface, or into wells as drinking water. But after considering the various barriers around the nuclear waste and its vitrified shell, he concludes:

> Plain commonsense shows that the chance of any substances in the glass getting past all these barriers in significant amounts, and in time still to be seriously radioactive when they finally emerge in drinking water, must be extraordinarily small.

The £240 million Windscale Vitrification Plant.

Suppose, none the less, that by some unforeseen circumstance the waste that was stored underground did break free underground? Sir Alan points out that although the waste is highly concentrated, the amount of waste is minute compared with the natural radioactive content of the surface layers of the earth:

> The world's first nuclear reactor existed without any containment whatsoever and was allowed to spill its contents freely into the surrounding rocks, waters and soil. All this happened 1,800 million years ago, at Oklo in west equatorial Africa, where a chance arrangement of rich uranium deposits and ground-water moderator produced conditions favourable for the formation of a *natural* light-water reactor. This performed for nearly a million years, generated about 15,000 megawatt years of energy, which is comparable with the lifetime output of a medium-sized nuclear power station. . . . [It] was discovered by geologists in 1972.

The implication is that the amount of man-made radioactivity caused on the surface by an accidental release from a waste repository would be extremely small compared with the amount of natural radioactivity.

But what if a radioactive escape was brought about by human action, either deliberately by terrorists or accidentally by mining engineers working nearby? Sir Alan thinks the first hardly credible. The second, he thinks, cannot happen so long as there is continuity of organised society; but in any case the sites being considered for nuclear waste are deliberately selected for their unattractiveness as sources of [suitable mining] materials.' Others would not agree. They believe the possibility of terrorist operation or accidental mining to be a credible hazard.

The Greens believe that storage above ground at existing nuclear sites is preferable until decisions can be made about ultimate disposal. This was an alternative considered by the House of Commons Environment Committee. One scenario they put forward for longer-lived waste was storage above ground for, say, 100 years, while research and development was undertaken on the potential disposal sites. This could be followed by a period of consignment of wastes to the stores where they could be monitored and checked for, say, another 50 to 100 years until, finally, 100 or 200 years after the waste was created, the facility would be sealed and closed. This 'interim storage' solution appears to find wide support.

The House of Commons Environment Committee had greater difficulty in establishing the difference between the terms 'storage' and 'disposal'. Lord Marshall, the former Chairman of the CEGB, told them he did not think there was a sharp distinction. The Committee found the Greenpeace definition more useful. This was that 'storage' meant 'leaving the waste in a condition where it is monitorable and retrievable on an almost daily basis.' Sir Hugh Rossi agreed that indefinite storage was not satisfactory. 'With waste which can be active for thousands of years,' he said, 'guaranteeing that the institutions [i.e. government departments or private firms] would be stable beyond periods which have so far proved to be whole lifetimes of civilisations would be impossible.'

High-level waste, as already noted, is currently a by-product of reprocessing, although it would exist just the same – but in larger quantities – if there were no reprocessing. Some critics of nuclear policy object to reprocessing, and they succeeded in having it stopped by the US government in the late 1970s because of fears associated with nuclear weapons proliferation. In addition, the major US civil utilities have not recently reprocessed fuel because of low uranium prices on the world market. In the somewhat unlikely event of reprocessing being stopped in Great Britain, it would of course still be necessary to find a means of storing the spent nuclear fuel from the nuclear power stations.

Lord Marshall was in charge of the CEGB until the industry was reorganised in 1990 and he is now the head of the worldwide nuclear supply organisations. Drax power station is the first due to be modified to reduce carbon dioxide emissions from coal-fired units.

Sellafield not only processes all UK spent fuel but also imports fuel elements sent by overseas customers who want the uranium and plutonium extracted. The Greens say that 1000 tonnes per year of this spent fuel are imported into the UK, but from this only 30 tonnes of high-level waste would result. They describe this business somewhat emotively as one in which 'the UK opens its doors to wash the world's dirty nuclear laundry.'

Another criticism of reprocessing is that it causes a large increase in the volume of low and intermediate-level waste. These pose a considerable storage and disposal problem, but one of a less dangerous nature.

Considerable concern exists about the methods employed in moving spent nuclear fuel from the power stations (in Britain or overseas) to the Sellafield plant where it is reprocessed. After reprocessing, only a maximum of 3 per cent of the original volume remains as waste – as the industry stresses, all the highly active liquid waste so far produced by Britain's nuclear power programme would fill just twelve double-decker buses.

The spent fuel elements mostly travel to Sellafield by train in heavily shielded steel, or steel and lead, flasks with walls about 1 foot thick. Elements which arrive in Britain by ship from overseas also move to Sellafield by train. Their movement is governed by regulations – for example, the transport of other types of dangerous goods on the same train is prohibited. Sir Hugh Rossi's committee, while generally impressed by the care and attention given to this rail transport, were concerned about two or three aspects. One was that there was the very remote 'and almost far-fetched possibility of a crash between two trains in a tunnel.'

The supply industry maintain that they have been moving this potentially dangerous cargo by train for over 30 years, and have moved at least 14,000 tonnes of irradiated fuel without a single significant accident or the slightest injury to any person or damage to any property. Every year, 500 trains ply between the ports or power stations and Sellafield. British Rail and the CEGB maintain a computer-controlled check on the progress of every shipment, so that at any given time the exact position of every flask can be obtained within an hour. British Rail commuters might be justified in expressing some scepticism about a system which claims to know the exact position of a train within an hour. Be this as it may, Sir Hugh Rossi recommended that radioactive waste, especially spent fuel, high-level waste and plutonium 'should be carried by rail in preference to all other modes of transport. The carriage by air of all except the very lowest levels of radioactive material should be prohibited.' The supply industry's view is that the worldwide transport of radioactive materials has been routinely carried out over many years by all forms of transport, including air, and that air transport should remain an available option for the transport of all nuclear materials, subject to national and international regulations.

While Sir Hugh Rossi considered it desirable to keep local authorities and emergency services informed about individual consignments of spent nuclear fuel by land, he accepted the explanation of the Department of Transport and British Rail that such a change in procedure would 'probably make the job of the emergency services more rather than less difficult.' Some critics would prefer such transport movements to be publicised.

Finally, Sir Hugh had some worries about sea transport. 'While the probability of an accident is very small,' he said, 'the consequences could be very serious indeed.' He recommended that the transport of radioactive materials through the English Channel might need 'greater control'.

Despite their increased openness about radioactive waste storage, the government's policies are still to some extent unclear. The TUC believe this issue to have been more incompetently handled than any other aspect of the nuclear programme, so it is not surprising that public concern has come to centre on this. It is also logical that, as the public has addressed itself to the relative advantage of nuclear energy over coal in terms of pollution effect, it will weigh the environmental problem of waste in the same balance. Both coal and

The CEGB carried out a test in which a heavy railway locomotive with three carriages, travelling at a speed of 100 mph, was deliberately crashed into a flask placed on the railway line in the most vulnerable position. The impact destroyed the locomotive, but the flask remained intact.

nuclear power generation produce waste, but which is the more environmentally hazardous?

The industry tends to rest its case, that radioactive waste can be managed safely and acceptably, on the small *quantity* involved:

> The amount of high-level waste produced in supplying someone with electricity for nuclear power for their whole life is only about the size of a cigarette packet. The corresponding volume of intermediate-level waste is about the size of a shoe box and for low-level waste about the size of a suitcase.

In contrast to these modest quantities, the nuclear industry and its supporters point out the very large quantities of harmful waste produced by the coal industry. Nuclear waste is certainly insignificant in size compared with the UK's 123 million tons of domestic rubbish (little of which is recycled and turned into anything useful) which have resulted in the allegation that it is 'the dirty man of Europe'. However it is the radioactive nature of some of the nuclear waste which is the basis of public concern and, despite the dangers from other types of waste, it is nuclear waste which inevitably comes under the spotlight.

# 8. MORE WASTE

The nuclear industry is constantly pressing its critics to put their comments 'in perspective'. For example, they explain that whereas British industry as a whole creates each year 5 to 10 million tonnes of general toxic wastes containing hazardous materials, the nuclear industry will create only 1 million tonnes of low-level waste up to the year 2000. The previous chapter has dealt with the more hazardous category of nuclear waste, but there are of course very much larger amounts of relatively less hazardous waste which have to be dealt with.

The official definition of low-level waste is material below specified levels of radioactivity – 4 GBq/tonne alpha and 12 GBq/tonne beta and gamma. The TUC energy committee maintained that even this 'technical specification' is not precise enough, since it includes items such as gloves, clothing and paper towels. 'As the the House of Commons Environment Committee pointed out in 1986,' say the TUC, 'there is no reference to how long these materials will be radioactive, nor to the concept of a particular important kind of radioactivity (alpha content).'

When Sir Hugh Rossi and his Environment Committee were investigating the subject in 1986, they visited the major radioactive low-level waste disposal site in the United Kingdom: BNFL's Drigg plant, four miles from Sellafield. This is where solid low-level waste is buried, including that from hospitals, research establishments and other industries. Sir Hugh noted:

> There is no sense of immediate risk. We could stand next to a drum of radioactive waste or peer down at the ugly but innocent-looking heaps of junk and feel that we were quite safe. We were reassured by the geiger counters registering only normal 'background' levels as we were checked back aboard the bus.

Nevertheless the committee was not very happy with arrangements at Drigg; even the then Minister, William Waldegrave, admitted 'it is clearly possible to do things better.' As a result, changes were made and BNFL made major improvements to the Drigg site. These included containerisation of waste, improvements in drainage and a new concrete-lined vault.

For final disposal of low-level solid waste, sea dumping was the policy favoured by NIREX, the company set up in 1982 (with government agreement) by four organisations – BNFL, the CEGB, the SSEB and the UKAEA. NIREX was reconstituted in 1985 as UK Nirex Ltd., with all the shares held by the partner organisations and by the Department of Energy on behalf of the government. It was the NIREX view that for certain categories of low-level and intermediate-level waste 'sea disposal is the best option.' The Rossi committee had, however, pointed out that this worked only 'very imperfectly'.

Criticisms might also be made about other

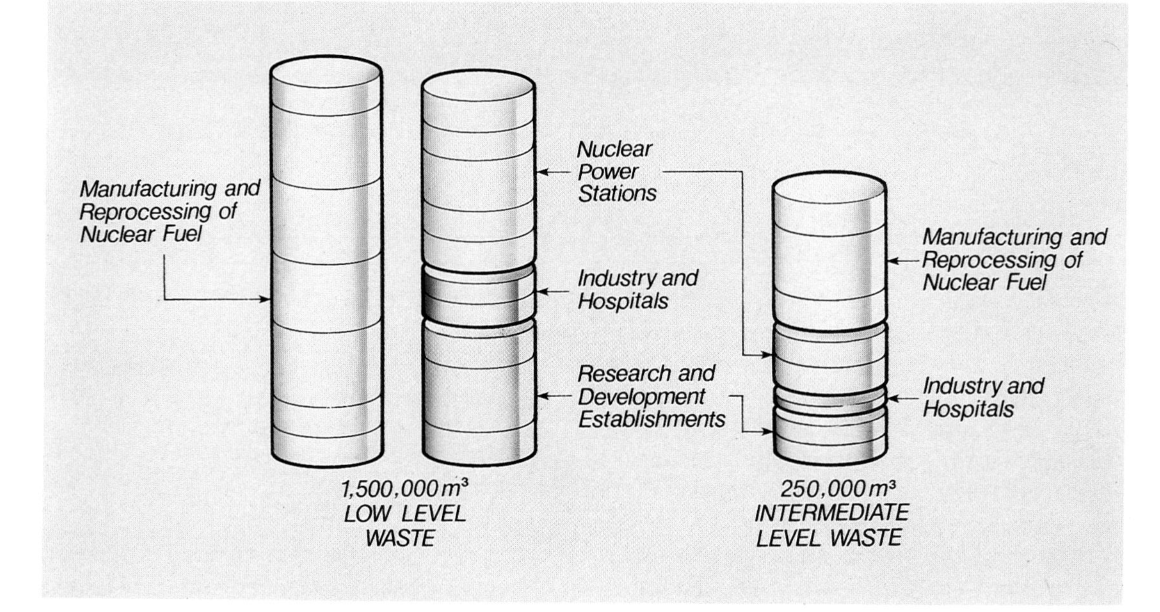


The relative quantities of low-level and intermediate-level waste produced by nuclear power stations, industry and hospitals and research and development establishments.

types of non-nuclear waste dumped at sea, but in fact the Government produced a spirited defence of sea dumping for general waste in a report published in September 1989. The nuclear industry, had it had the opportunity, would have used the same arguments to support putting its waste out to sea.

However the National Union of Seamen (NUS) had forced the abandonment of sea dumping by the United Kingdom as early as 1982 because, it said, while merchant seaman are not experts in this matter, 'we do not have to be scientists to know that any major miscalculation would be irreversible, certainly for hundreds and thousands of years.' Their other objection was a moral one:

> The NUS questions the morality of any nation . . . using international waters as a disposal site for its nuclear waste, when the environmental repercussions of such a policy would not respect national boundaries.

Once the NUS had declined to handle the disposal of nuclear waste at sea, NIREX and others involved were forced to rethink their policies.

The government had set NIREX a target, requiring that their disposal operations should place the public at a risk no greater than one chance in a million per year of being exposed to any adverse health effect leading to premature death. NIREX describe this as corresponding to 'roughly the risk of smoking just one cigarette a year'. They also point out that it is less than the risk associated with variations in natural background radiation within the UK. To meet these stringent requirements, NIREX considered other methods of disposal.

NIREX had run into problems when it had selected and announced plans for possible shallow-ground sites for low-level waste; it had been forced to relinquish these because of objections from third parties. NIREX then announced that it would call off further investigation into four other shallow-ground sites, saying that it had now been established that this kind of burial had no economic advantage over deep underground facilities. It seemed that the time had come for the development of the first UK underground site.

Then in 1988, NIREX announced that further decisions about where to site underground waste would be postponed so that it could take soundings from the public. If the public were to pay for nuclear waste disposal then, said NIREX, they should have a voice in the decision-making process. They issued a discussion document entitled *The Way Forward* which invited comments on three of the alternative disposal techniques available. These were:

(i) a deep-mined cavity underground, using proven mining techniques
(ii) an offshore, sub-seabed cavity accessed by tunnels driven out from a coastal location
(iii) a sub-seabed cavity accessed from the surface of the sea by means of a drilling platform or an artificial island.

Comment on the NIREX document by FOE, Greenpeace and CORE (Cumbrians Opposed to a Radioactive Environment) repeated that NIREX was confining its options to disposal when a better alternative, in their view, was temporarily to store low-level and intermediate-level waste above ground at existing nuclear sites.

In the event, and depending on the results of detailed on-site geological research, NIREX identified a possible site in the general area of Sellafield (where the waste from reprocessing is already stored) and a second potential site at the UKAEA plant at Dounreay. NIREX saw its task as being to design, locate and develop a simple deep underground disposal centre for both low and intermediate-level waste. However, BNFL's plan to store all low-level waste at Drigg may change NIREX's plans.

BNFL's Drigg plant near Sellafield, where solid low-level waste is stored. In 1990 BNFL signalled a major change in nuclear waste policy when it said that Drigg would be able to take all low-level waste arising in the UK until the year 2050, by compacting it first in a new plant.

Any discussion about what to do with radioactive waste has to recognise the prevalence of what is called the NIMBY Syndrome – put it somewhere but *Not In My Back Yard.* The TUC's comment on this is that the benefits of an industrial society

> cannot yet be had without large quantities of waste . . . at least some of which is dangerous enough to need isolating from the public forever. This is a problem for the whole of society and . . .

. . . NIMBY cannot prevail over everything. It [the TUC] has enough trust in the British public (as well as the public in other countries) to believe that agreed solutions can be found, provided the authorities involved act in a responsible manner and take the public into their confidence.

Whatever the final policy on solid low-level and intermediate-level waste disposal, it will not take effect until the turn of the century.

As regards solid low-level waste, the CEGB, in its Hinkley Point C case, described how this is currently processed to reduce its overall volume by incineration at some stations, compaction and shredding, after which it is packed and transported to Drigg, although in the future it could be sent to the new NIREX deep storage facility. The packaging is mostly in 200 litre drums.

Decanning magnox fuel rods. The resulting magnox cladding is one type of intermediate-level waste.

NIREX estimates that by the year 2030 the volume of low-level waste will be 1.5 million cubic metres, and of intermediate-level waste 250,000 cubic metres. Remember that, by contrast, the UK produces between five and ten million tons of general toxic waste annually.

At present, intermediate and low-level waste is stored at power stations in concrete vaults and steel tanks, generally below ground. Ash from the incinerators in which low-level waste is burnt, prior to storage, is also stored in concrete vaults. If the volumes of such waste are to grow as NIREX forecasts, and the solid waste is to be transported to the chosen NIREX site, then the public will want to know more about the transportation process.

NIREX says that low-level waste contains such little radioactivity that no special precautions or shielding are required when handling and transporting it. The standard 200 litre drums have been used for many years, in groups of twelve drums 'placed in simple frames and in standard freight containers for road or rail transport'.

Intermediate-level waste, such as fuel cladding, reactor components and gas filters, is by definition more radioactive than low-level waste. NIREX propose 'a simple but effective combination of engineered and natural barriers to keep the radioactivity out of the ground water' (which, if reached, might ultimately carry it into the food chain). They summarise as follows:

The waste is solid and generally insoluble.
It will be packed in steel drums or concrete boxes.
It is to be mixed with concrete inside its container.
The complete packages will be put deep underground in a mine.

They add that the use of concrete is important because radionuclides do not readily

Magnox cladding

Magnox cladding encapsulated in cement.

dissolve in it, so that a barrier is created which is estimated to last for thousands of years. They conclude: 'most of the radioactivity will fade away quite naturally.'

Intermediate waste is expected to be stored in standard 500 litre drums, transported in groups of four in heavy steel reusable containers. Since some bulky waste of this type could not easily be fitted into drums, a series of large reinforced-concrete boxes is being developed, each weighing up to 100 tonnes, inside which the waste will be grouted with concrete. NIREX says that all containers are checked for radioactive contamination before transport and on arrival. It claims it is developing 'a fully-integrated transport system making optimum use of road and rail transport with the prime object of maintaining the highest safety standards.'

Some critics are doubtful about the safety of carrying intermediate waste by road, particularly as they are not entirely happy about its technical definition.

BNFL gives a helpful definition of

Store for the vitrified glass blocks at Sellafield.

intermediate waste as consisting of material such as fuel element cladding, plutonium-contaminated equipment and sludges resulting from various treatment processes.

Such waste will be placed in encapsulation plants being built at Sellafield, which will contain it safely by encasing it in cement within steel drums. The drums are then stored 'pending disposal'. NIREX reports that about 2500 cubic metres of intermediate-level waste are produced in Britain each year. For comparison, this is about 70 times the amount of high-level waste, but only one tenth of the figure for the low-level category.

Low-level liquid and gaseous wastes are also dispersed in the environment. They are of a very low level of radioactivity. The Department of the Environment give the organisations producing such wastes the necessary authorisation to allow them to pump them from the shore out to sea or discharge them through a chimney stack. NIREX plays no part in the management of such waste. The organisations which do, primarily BNFL, have been subject to a good deal of criticism about the extent to which they have pumped low-level radioactive waste out to sea. Indeed it has been said that the UK, primarily from Sellafield, has discharged more radioactivity to the sea than any other nation, as a result of which 'the Irish Sea is the most radioactive sea in the world.' The industry comment on this is that it is untrue and that the amount of radioactivity is negligible. The House of Lords Select Committee report on Nuclear Power in Europe (July 1986) noted that 'the natural radioactivity of the Dead Sea and the Great Salt Lake (Utah) result in greater total activity per unit volume than concentrations in the Irish Sea, even in the vicinity of the Sellafield outfall.'

BNFL's discharges have been detected in Britain itself, in Ireland, and as far away as Sweden, where the Rossi committee noted: 'The Swedes could identify radioactive traces in fish off their coasts being largely attributable to Sellafield, greater even than contamination from adjacent Swedish nuclear power stations.' The industry comments that this is more a reflection of the sensitivity of their measuring instruments than an indication of high levels, as these are in fact negligible.

The industry further counters criticism by drawing attention to the much more serious discharges to the sea made by other industries and, more significantly, to the steps they have taken to reduce their own discharges over the years. New plants, such as the Site Ion Exchange Effluent Plant (SIXEP) at Sellafield have helped to reduce discharges to less than one thousandth of peak levels and further plant is being constructed to make even more reductions. They point out that the average radiation dose to members of the public who eat fish landed at Whitehaven are about 0.01 mSv – or 5% of the dose from a chest X-ray.

Some 40 hectares (100 acres) of land are considered necessary by NIREX for a land-based repository such as this. Fifteen trains a week would be needed, or ten trains and one hundred deliveries by lorry.

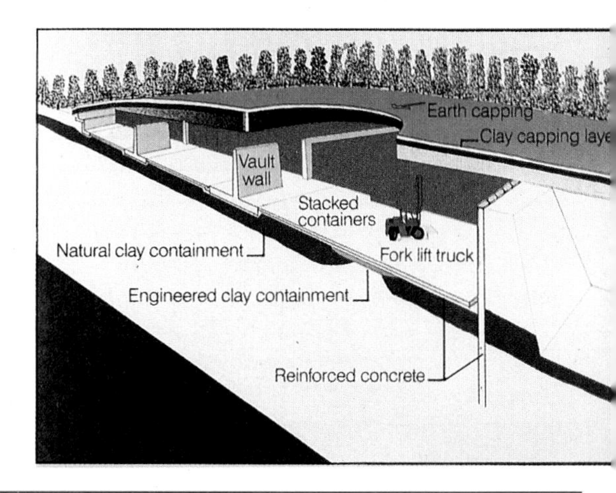

In the USA, critics complain that the Columbia river in Washington State has been so contaminated by leaks, accidents, operation and design failures of the Hanford Nuclear Reservation that it has become 'the most contaminated river in the world'. Critics of Sellafield claim that the contamination there is at a much higher level, although BNFL has made considerable efforts to persuade the media that the amounts in question are not significant.

To sum up, the nuclear industry believes that, 'there are no reasons why radioactive wastes cannot continue to be managed and supervised in a safe and acceptable manner.' Yet if intermediate-level waste, unlike most low-level waste, is to be stored so that it 'may be retrieved in the future', then the question of how it can be disposed of, once retrieved, is as yet unanswered.

Some regard the industry's attitude as complacent. The TUC believe that 'a new institutional structure is needed to co-ordinate policy and administer the management of waste' since NIREX, as it is presently constituted, 'is not a satisfactory body for determining the strategy.' At the more extreme end of the scale is the American Jim Garrison who claims: 'there is at present *no* place to store radioactive wastes.'

The industry responds that hundreds of millions of pounds are being spent on a whole range of waste management techniques, both nationally and internationally. BNFL is responsible for high-level waste disposal, which will not be undertaken for many years to come, but in the meantime is following with interest the international project at the Stripa mine in Sweden which is assessing the feasibility of disposing of waste in granite rocks. In 1988, a repository for low and intermediate-level waste also came into operation at Försmark on the Baltic coast. Deep geological burial remains the most likely solution, on the basis of present knowledge, but less conventional ones include transmutation, where long-lived radioisotopes are subjected to further irradiation and converted to short-lived radioisotopes or stable elements.

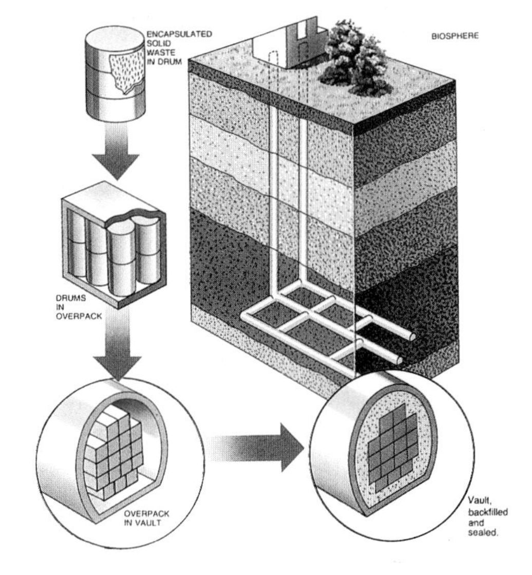

Diagram of a proposed repository for deep storage of low and intermediate-level waste.

It is, of course, no defence for an industry accused of inadequate handling of waste (and the nuclear organisations deny the charge) to point to the failure of other industries to deal with *their* waste. Yet the fact remains that most of Britain's thousands of dumps for domestic and general industrial waste fail to meet the standards of a landfill directive proposed by the European Commission. This is the conclusion of experts from the Environmental Safety Centre of the AEA, Harwell, which recently examined 100 tips mostly run by local councils. Perhaps the lesson to be drawn is that there should be higher standards set for all waste disposal, whether of nuclear origin or not, in a country often criticised as being the dirtiest in Europe.

# 9. THE CONTINUING DEBATE

The world as we know it depends on energy but there is no consensus of view about how adequate supplies can be maintained and paid for now, or new resources husbanded for generations to come. Nor is there agreement about how our environment can be protected from the harmful effects of energy generation which may, if unchecked, make it difficult for human life to continue.

This book has attempted to set out the main issues affecting the newest form of energy – nuclear power – and to describe the points of view of those who debate its future. It is clear that the debate is highly polarised between those in its favour and those against it. Many major institutions – the government, some opposition parties and much of the media – believe that nuclear power will continue to play a major rôle. At the same time there is considerable ignorance. A recent poll of school children between the ages of 14 and 18, for example, showed that 40 per cent think that nuclear power stations have something to do with bombs and 24 per cent think bombs are made in them.

No attempt has been made in this book to cast a vote in the debate one way or another. The point has however been stressed that nuclear power exists and decisions have to be made, here and in other countries, about its future. It is a fact of life. Those who still have an open mind on the subject may find it useful to consider the following questions which, we suggest, highlight the main issues in the debate. By trying to answer them, and to measure future decisions and policies against them, it may be possible to come to some conclusions about what is best for the United Kingdom and the world at large.

### THE NEED

1. Has the British government an energy policy and if so what part does nuclear power play in it? How should decisions be made about the kinds of power stations which will have to be built to meet future needs?
2. If there is a gap between future UK energy needs and the planned output, has nuclear power an inevitable rôle to play in filling it?
3. If there are alternatives to nuclear energy which would make a practical contribution to UK energy needs, would their development affect the proposed nuclear programme?
4. How large a part can energy conservation play in the apparent gap between future demand and planned supply?

### THE ENVIRONMENT

1. How far are the various forms of energy generation detrimental to the environment? It is possible to make objective assessments about which are worse than others?
2. Can these environmental ill-effects be reduced or stopped? Is the environmental case for nuclear power all gain?

3. How important is the development of fusion energy to ensure a cleaner environment in the future?
4. Was the House of Commons Select Committee on Energy right to propose, in August 1990, that Britain should abandon all research into fast-breeder nuclear reactor technology by 1997?

**THE COSTS**

1. What will be the most significant factors affecting the relative costs of fossil-fuel-powered and nuclear-powered stations over the next decade?
2. Can the cost of programmes to improve the environment always be passed on to the consumer?
3. Can the relative costs of the different forms of generating power be left to 'market forces' or should there be some international debate about the best means of meeting the world's energy needs?
4. Should the UK fast-breeder reactor research programme be abandoned unless they can be shown to be economically viable within 30 years?

**SAFETY**

1. Is the record of the UK nuclear industry a reassuring one and are there any specific steps to be taken which could improve safety in the future?
2. Is nuclear waste dealt with in the safest and most efficient way or does more need to be done?
3. Will decommissioning of redundant nuclear stations present novel problems or can it be left in the hands of the industry?

**GENERAL**

1. Are there any aspects of nuclear power which are unique to the UK and will the privatisation of the electricity industry raise new issues?
2. Are there wider considerations affecting the growth of nuclear power in the world at large which call for international debate and agreement?
3. Does the Gulf crisis add a new dimension to the debate about whether nuclear power has a key role to play in the world's future energy policies?

# DEPARTMENT OF ENERGY

## NEWS RELEASE

6 September 1990

John Wakeham, Energy Secretary, announced today that he has given consent and planning permission for the construction of a PWR nuclear power station at Hinkley Point in Somerset. Mr Wakeham emphasises that investment in further PWR stations will not be approved in 1994 unless they are assessed to be economic over their life as a whole.

The benefits of fuel diversity and the environmental advantages of non-fossil fired generation will need to be taken into account in this assessment. Mr Wakeham makes it clear that renewables and nuclear both have a part to play in containing sulphur dioxide and carbon dioxide emissions and should not be regarded as competitors.

# REFERENCES

**Conversion factors and constants**

1 watt = 1 joule per second
1 kilowatt (kW) = 1,000 watts
1 megawatt (MW) = 1,000 kW
1 gigawatt (GW) = 1,000,000 kW
1 kilowatt (kWh) = 1,000 watt hours
1 megawatt hour (MWh) = 1,000 kWh
1 terawatt hour (TWh) = 1,000,000,000 kWh
1 tonne of coal equivalent = approximately 250 therms of 0.6 tonne of petroleum or 2 MWh of electricity produced
1Gj = 9.478 therms
tU = tonnes of Uranium
mtce = million tonnes coal equivalent
Joule = a measure of work done
1 joule = 10 million ergs
MW (thermal) = heat input into a generating unit, measured in MW
1 therm = 100,000 British thermal units

**Initials, Acronyms and Abbreviations**

ACS Average Cold Spell
AGR Advanced Gas-cooled Reactor
ALARA As Low As Reasonably Achievable
BNFL British Nuclear Fuels plc
CEGB Central Electricity Generating Board
CHP Combined Heat and Power
Ci Curie
CPRE Council for the Protection of Rural England
DNC Declared Net Capability
ECCS Emergency Core Cooling System
EEC European Economic Community
FBR Fast-Breeder Reactor
FGD Flue Gas Desulphurisation
FOE Friends of the Earth
GW Gigawatt
HSE Health and Safety Executive
HTGR High-Temperature Gas-Cooled Reactor
ICRP International Commission on Radiological Protection MW Megawatt
mSv Millisievert
MOD Ministry of Defence
NAC Net Avoidable Cost
NRC Nuclear Radioactivity Commission (USA)
NEC Net Effective Cost
NII Nuclear Installations Inspectorate
NIREX Nuclear Industry Radioactive Waste Executive
NNC National Nuclear Corporation
NRPB National Radiological Protection Board
OECD Organisation for Economic Co-operation and Development OPEC Organisation of Petroleum Exporting Countries
PWR Pressurised Water Reactor
SGHWR Steam Generating Heavy Water Reactor
so Sent Out — sometimes referred to as 'net'
SSEB South of Scotland Electricity Board
Sv Sievert
UKAEA United Kingdom Atomic Energy Authority

Acknowledgement is made to the authors and publisher of the official reports and books listed in the bibliography. In addition, use has been made of the publications of the CEGB, AEA, BNFL and NIREX. Illustrations and diagrams have been kindly provided by each of these organisations.

**EVERYMAN'S GUIDE TO NUCLEAR TERMS**

**Activation** The process of inducing radioactivity by irradiation.

**Activity** In a given quantity of material, the number of spontaneous nuclear disintegrations occurring per unit time. See also Becquerel and Curie.

**Advanced gas-cooled reactor (AGR)** The AGR is a development of the Magnox reactor designed to operate at higher temperatures and so improve the thermal efficiency and economic performance of the reactor. It uses slightly enriched uranium oxide fuel contained in stainless steel cans, a graphite moderator and carbon dioxide gas as the coolant.

**After-heat (decay heat)** Heat generated in a reactor after it has shut down; it is produced by the decay of fission products in the fuel elements.

**Alpha particle** A positively charged particle emitted during the decay of some radioactive nuclei; it is composed of two protons and two neutrons and is identical with the nucleus of the helium-4 atom.

**Atom** A unit of matter consisting of a single nucleus surrounded by a number of electrons equal to the number of protons in the nucleus. Atoms are the basic building blocks of all substances, and cannot be broken down further by chemical means.

**Atomic number** The number of protons in the nucleus of an atom. In a neutral atom, it is also equal to the number of electrons in orbit around the nucleus. Since the chemical properties of an atom are determined by the number of these electrons, the atomic number establishes an atom's chemical identity. All isotopes of a given element have the same atomic number.

**Background radiation** The natural ionizing radiation of man's environment due to cosmic rays from outer space, naturally radioactive elements in the ground and air, and naturally radioactive elements in a person's body.

**Becquerel (Bq)** A measure of the rate at which a radioactive material disintegrates. One Bq corresponds to the decay of one nuclide per second. Replaces the Curie (Ci) = $3.7 \times 10^{10}$ Bq.

**Beta particle** Electrons emitted from a radionuclide during beta decay.

**Biological shield** A mass of material which reduces ionizing radiation in a given region to acceptable levels. In particular, the term is applied to the shield placed round the core of a nuclear reactor for the purpose of absorbing neutrons and gamma radiation.

**Boiling water reactor (BWR)** A nuclear reactor cooled and moderated by light water. The water is allowed to boil in the core to generate steam which passes direct to the turbine.

**Breeding reactor (or breeder)** A reactor which produces more fissile nuclei than it consumes.

**Burn-up** Cumulative output of heat from reactor fuel, usually measured in megawatt — days per tonne of uranium.

**Candu** A Canadian developed nuclear power reactor system. The name is derived from CANada Deuterium Uranium, indicating that the moderator is deuterium or heavy water, and that the fuel is natural uranium.

**Carbon** A non-metallic element, atomic number 6. In the form of graphite it is used as a moderator in thermal reactors to slow down the fast neutrons produced during fission to thermal energies. The Magnox and AGR systems both use graphite as a moderator.

**Carbon-14** Formed from the interaction of neutrons in cosmic radiation with nitrogen in the upper atmosphere. Carbon-14, which has a half-life of 5568 years, diffuses to the lower atmosphere where it may become incorporated in living matter; thus it is a contributing factor to the level of natural background radiation.

**Carbon dioxide ($CO_2$)** A relatively inert gas used as a coolant in some thermal reactors. For example, the Magnox and AGR systems both use carbon dioxide as the coolant.

**Chain reaction** A self sustaining reaction that initiates its own repetition. In nuclear fission, a neutron induces a nucleus to fission as a result of which neutrons are released which cause more fissions.

**China syndrome** Consequences predicted for a

meltdown, when molten mass of radioactive material burns through the vessel and its containment into the earth and proceeds through towards the other side.

**Cladding** An external layer of material applied directly to nuclear fuel or other material. It provides protection from a chemically reactive environment, containment of radioactive products during irradiation, or structural support. (See also Fuel can.)

**Containment** A gas-tight shell around a reactor and its associated steam raising plant to contain any radioactive products which escape from the nuclear equipment due to any form of failure or accident.

**Contamination** Radioactive material which has been deposited on a normally non-radioactive surface. It may be liquid or particulate in form.

**Control rod** A rod used to control the reactivity of a reactor. The rod is usually made of steel and contains a good neutron absorber such as boron or cadmium. Movement of the rod enables the power level to be held constant or to be varied as required.

**Coolant** Any gas or liquid fluid circulated through the core of a reactor to extract the heat liberated in the fission process.

**Cooling** A colloquial term to describe the process of storing radioactive material, such as used fuel elements to allow the radioactivity to decay. The storage is often carried out under water in a cooling pond.

**Cooling pond** A large container, filled with water, in which irradiated fuel is set aside until its activity has decreased to a desired level.

**Core** The portion of a nuclear reactor containing the fissile material.

**Cosmic rays** Radiation emanating from high energy sources outside the earth's atmosphere including the sun and stars.

**Critical** The condition of a reactor which is just capable of sustaining a chain reaction.

**Critical mass** The minimum amount of fissile material needed to sustain a chain reaction.

**Curie (Ci)** The rate at which a radioactive material disintegrates. A curie is the radioactivity on one gram of radium and is named after Pierre and Marie Curie, the discoverers of the radioactive elements radium, radon and polonium. One curie corresponds to 37 thousand million disintegrations per second. A millicurie (mCi) is one thousandth of a curie; a microcurie (μCi) is one millionth of a curie. This has been replaced by the SI unit becquerel (Bq) = $27 \times 10^{-12}$ Ci. Note: Sometimes the term is used to designate a quantity of a radionuclide.

**Decay** The decrease in activity of a radioactive material as it transforms spontaneously from one nuclide into another or into a different energy state of the same nuclide. Radioactive decay is usually accompanied by the emission of charged particles and gamma rays.

**Deuterium** A stable naturally occurring isotope of hydrogen with a mass number of two. It combines with oxygen to form heavy water ($D_2O$), which is used as a neutron moderator in some reactors.

**Disintegration** See **Decay**

**Dose** The amount of ionizing radiation energy absorbed (per unit mass). See also gray, sievert, rad and rem.

**Electron** An elementary particle carrying one unit of negative electrical charge. Electrons determine the chemical behaviour of elements, and their "flow" through a conductor constitutes electricity.

**Element** A substance all of whose atoms have the same atomic number and therefore the same chemical properties. There are 92 naturally occurring elements each having its own distinctive atom. Elements are simple substances which cannot be resolved into simpler substances by normal chemical means. All substances are made up of various chemical combinations of elements. See also Atoms.

**Enriched fuel** Nuclear fuel containing more than the natural abundance of fissile atoms.

**Fast breeder reactor** A reactor in which the fission chain reaction is sustained by fast neutrons, that is neutrons that have lost relatively little energy since being produced in the fission process. The fuel is highly enriched and a blanket of fertile material surrounding the core captures neutrons to become fissile fuel.

**Fast neutrons** Neutrons resulting from fission that are not intentionally slowed down by a moderator.

**Fissile** Capable of undergoing fission, usually following the absorption of a neutron.

**Fissile material** Nuclear fuels in which the nuclei, when hit by neutrons, split and release energy plus further neutrons which can result in a chain reaction. Uranium-233, uranium-235 and plutonium-239 are examples of important fissile materials, but only uranium-235 occurs in nature.

**Fission** The splitting of a heavy nucleus into two parts (fragments) accompanied by the release of energy and two or more neutrons. It may occur spontaneously or be induced by capture of bombarding particles, particularly neutrons.

**Fission fragments** The nuclides formed directly in the fission process. When uranium-235 fissions, the fragments are rarely equal in mass, but consist of a heavier group with mass numbers around 140 and a lighter group with mass numbers around 95. The greatest part of the energy released in fission appears in the form of kinetic energy of the fission fragments. The fragments are excessively rich in neutrons and decay by successive beta-particle emissions until a stable nuclide is formed.

**Fission products** The small nuclei produced in fission, either directly or by the disintegration of the fission fragments. Over 300 stable and radioactive fission products have been identified. They represent isotopes of some 35 different chemical elements ranging from arsenic-85 to gadolinium-160.

**Fuel assembly** An assembly of fuel elements and supporting mechanisms.

**Fuel can** The container into which fuel in the form of rods or pellets is inserted and sealed to prevent the escape of fission products into the coolant and protect the fuel from corrosion by the coolant.

**Fuel element** An assembly comprising the fissile material (for example, natural or enriched uranium) contained in a can, the latter often having fins to improve the heat transfer between the element and the coolant.

**Fuel pellets** Uranium dioxide or other nuclear fuel in a powdered form, which has been pressed, sintered and ground to a cylindrical shape for insertion into the fuel can of a fuel assembly.

**Fuelling machine** Equipment used to load (and unload) the fuel assemblies into the fuel channels of a reactor. For some reactors, fuelling machines can load the fuel while the reactor is operating.

**Fusion** The combination of two light nuclei to form a single heavier nucleus.

**Gamma rays** High energy short wavelength electromagnetic radiation emitted by the nuclei of many radioactive atoms during radioactive decay. Gamma rays are highly penetrating, but are absorbed by dense materials such as lead.

**Gas-cooled reactor** A nuclear reactor in which gas, such as carbon dioxide, is used as the coolant. Two examples of this type of reactor are the Magnox reactor and the AGR.

**Genetic effects (hereditary)** Effects that are due to radiation damage to the cells of the reproductive organs of the body. Such damage may affect the offspring of an irradiated person and subsequently later generations. (See also **Somatic Effects.)**

**Graphite** A dense rigid crystalline form of carbon used as a moderator in thermal reactors.

**Half life** The time taken for half the atoms of a radioactive substance to disintegrate; in other words, the time taken for a given quantity of a substance to lose half its radioactive strength. Each radionuclide has a unique half life ranging from millionths of a second to millions of years.

**Health physics** The branch of physics concerned with the effects of ionizing radiation on living matter and the protection of personnel from the harmful effects of such radiation.

**Heat exchanger** A piece of equipment that transfers heat from one medium to another. A typical example is the boiler in gas-cooled reactors in which heat from the pressurized carbon dioxide gas coolant is used to convert water into steam to run the turbine.

**Heavy water** Deuterium oxide or water containing a substantial proportion of deuterium atoms. Heavy water is used as a moderator in some reactor systems.

**HTGR** High-temperature gas-cooled reactor.

**Ion** An atom or molecule, that has lost or gained one or more electrons and therefore possesses a net positive or negative charge. Sometimes an electron is described as a negative ion.

**Ionization** The process by which an atom, electrically neutral under normal conditions, becomes electrically charged by gaining or losing one or more orbital electrons. The loss of an electron produces a positive ion, while one gained produces a negative ion.

**Ionizing radiation** Any particle or radiation with sufficient energy to ionize matter through which it travels.

**Irradiation** The exposure of matter to radiation: for example, exposure to neutrons of material placed in a reactor.

**Isotope** Species of an atom with the same number of protons in their nuclei, hence having the same atomic number and belonging to the same element, but differing in the number of neutrons. Such atoms have identical chemical properties but their nuclear characteristics may be vastly different: for example, hydrogen (H-1) and deuterium or heavy hydrogen (H-2) and the isotopes of uranium, U-235 and U-238.

**Kilowatt (kw)** One thousand watts.

**Lead (Pb)** A heavy metallic element, atomic number 82, widely used as a radiation shielding material because of its high density.

**LWR** Light-water reactor (See **PWR** and **BWR**).

**Magnox** The magnesium alloy used as the canning material for the fuel elements in the Magnox reactors.

**Magnox reactor** One of the first types of reactor to be used for the large-scale production of electricity. The

Magnox reactor uses natural uranium as fuel, graphite as the moderator and carbon dioxide gas under pressure as the coolant.

**Mass number** The total number of protons and neutrons in the nucleus of an atom; for example, uranium-235 has 92 protons + 143 neutrons.

**Megawatt (MW)** One million watts or one thousand kilowatts; a method of indicating the electrical power rating of motors and generators.

**Moderator** A material such as heavy water, graphite or light water used in a reactor to slow down or moderate the fast neutrons produced by fission, thus increasing the likelihood of further fission.

**Molecule** The smallest piece of a substance that still retains the characteristics of that substance. A further sub-division would break down the substance into its constituent atoms. For example, the sub-division of a molecule of water ($H_2O$) would produce atoms of hydrogen and oxygen.

**Monitor** An instrument used to measure the level of ionizing radiation or quantity of radioactive material.

**Natural background radiation** See **Background radiation.**

**Natural uranium** Uranium as it occurs in nature, containing the fertile isotope U-238 and the fissile isotope U-235 in the proportions 139:1 or 0.7 per cent by weight of U-235.

**Neutron** An uncharged (neutral) elementary particle with a mass nearly equal to that of the proton and associated with it in the nuclei of atoms.

**Nuclear energy** The energy liberated by a nuclear reaction such as fission.

**Nuclear power** The power obtained from the release of nuclear energy.

**Nuclear reactor** A device designed and operated for the purpose of initiating and maintaining a controlled nuclear fission chain reaction in a fissile material.

**Nucleus** The positively charged central portion of an atom which has almost the whole mass of the atom but only a minute fraction of its volume. All nuclei are made up of protons and neutrons, except for the nucleus of ordinary hydrogen (H-1) which contains only one proton.

**Nuclide** An isotope of an element.

**Plutonium (Pu)** A heavy radioactive metallic element with an atomic number of 94 whose principal isotope Pu-239 is a major fissile material. It is produced artificially in reactors through neutron absorption of uranium-238.

**Potassium-40** Potassium-40 is a naturally occurring isotope of potassium with a half life of $1.27 \times 10^9$ years. It is found in small quantities in the human body and is a contributing factor to the level of natural background radiation.

**Pressure tube reactor** A power reactor in which the fuel is located inside tubes designed to withstand the circulation of the high pressure coolant. The tubes are assembled in a tank (calandria) containing the moderator at low pressure.

**Pressure vessel** The vessel containing the fuel elements, moderator and coolant of a reactor. Its purpose is to enable the reactor to be operated at pressures above atmospheric in order to improve the heat transfer properties of the coolant. It is generally constructed of steel or of pre-stressed concrete.

**Pressurized water reactor (PWR)** A power reactor cooled and moderated by light water in a pressure vessel surrounding the core. The water is pressurized in a close primary loop to prevent boiling, and is circulated through a heat exchanger which generates steam in a secondary loop connected to the turbine.

**Proton** An elementary particle with a charge equal and opposite to that of an electron. Its atomic mass is 1847 times that of an electron. It comprises the nucleus of an ordinary hydrogen atom whose mass number is defined as one. It is a constituent of all nuclei.

**Rad** A unit of absorbed dose of ionizing radiation. (Abbreviated from Radiation Absorbed Dose). Now replaced by the SI unit gray (Gy). See also **Rem.**

**Radiation** The emission and propagation of energy through space or matter in the form of electromagnetic waves and fast moving particles such as gamma and X-rays.

**Radiation damage** The effects of radiation on the properties of materials, especially in nuclear reactors.

**Radioactivity** The property, possessed by some atoms of disintegrating spontaneously with the emission of a charged particle and/or gamma radiation.

**Radioiodine** A radioactive isotope of iodine, I-131, with a half life of 8 days. It is a volatile fission product produced in reactors.

**Radioisotope** A radioactive isotope of an element.

**Radionuclide** See **Radioisotope.**

**Radium** Radioactive alpha-emitting heavy element.

**Reactor** See **Nuclear reactor.**

**Reactor vessel** See **Pressure vessel.**

**Recycling** The reuse of fissionable material recovered from irradiated nuclear fuel by reprocessing.

**Rem** A unit of absorbed dose of ionizing radiation in biological matter. (Abbreviated from Roentgen Equivalent

Man.) Now replaced by the SI unit sievert (Sv). See also **Rad.**

**Reprocessing** The extraction of fissionable material from spent fuel for later use by recycling.

**Roentgen** A unit of exposure to gamma or X-rays. Named after William Conrad Roentgen, the discoverer of X-rays in 1895.

**Scrubbers** See FGD.

**Shielding** A mass of material surrounding a source of radiation that reduces radiation intensity to protect personnel, equipment or nuclear experiments from radiation injury, damage or interference. Dense concrete, several feet thick is used for shielding the core of a reactor. (See also **Biological shield.)**

**Sievert (Sv)** The unit of absorbed dose of radiation exposure in biological matter.

**Slow neutrons** Neutrons that have been slowed down by a moderator so as to increase the probability of their collision with a fissile nucleus and induce fission.

**Sodium** A metallic element with an atomic number of 11 and low melting point. In its liquid form, it is used as a coolant in fast breeder reactors.

**Somatic effects** Effects that arise from damage to the cells of the body. The term "Somatic" is used to distinguish those tissues or cells which die when the whole body dies, from the genetic material which may be passed on to future generations. Thus somatic effects can only arise in the person whose body cells have been damaged. In contrast, damage to a person's genetic cells produces effects in their offspring and possibly in subsequent generations, but has no effect on the person concerned.

**Spent fuel** Nuclear fuel that has been irradiated in a reactor to the extent that it can no longer sustain a chain reaction effectively, i.e. some of the fissionable isotopes have been consumed and fission product poisons have been accumulated.

**Thermal neutrons** See **Slow neutrons.**

**Thermal reactor** A reactor in which the chain reaction is sustained primarily by fission brought about by thermal neutrons. Such a reactor uses a moderator to slow down the neutrons produced in fission.

**Thorium (Th)** A heavy metallic element with an atomic number of 90, whose naturally occurring isotope Th-232 is slightly radioactive and fertile. When irradiated in a reactor, it leads to the production of uranium-233.

**Tritium** A naturally occurring radioactive isotope of hydrogen with a mass number of 3. It has one proton and two neutrons in its nucleus, and is produced in heavy water moderated reactors by neutron capture of deuterium. It is also produced from impurities in the graphite moderators in gas-cooled reactors.

**Uranium (U)** A heavy slightly radioactive metallic element with an atomic number of 92. As found in nature, it is a mixture of the isotopes U-235 (0.7 per cent) and U-238 (99.3 per cent). The artificially produced U-233 (See **Thorium**) and the naturally occurring U235 are fissile; U-238 is fertile.

**Uranium dioxide ($UO_2$)** Used a fuel in AGRs because of its chemical and radiation stability, good gaseous fission product retention and high melting points.

**Watts (W)** Measure of rate of transfer of energy.

# FURTHER READING

(in order of date of publication)

*Reports*

1953 *A Programme for Nuclear Power:* Ministry of Supply (HMSO)

1976 Report of the Committee of Inquiry on the Structure of the Electricity Supply Industry [Plowden Report] (HMSO)

1976 Royal Commission on Environmental Pollution: *Nuclear Power and the Environment:* Sixth Report [Flowers Report] (HMSO)

1976 Ranger Uranium Environmental Enquiry. First Report [Fox Report] (Australian Government)

1978 *Planning and Plutonium:* Evidence at Windscale Inquiry (Town and Country Planning Association).

1978 Windscale Inquiry (HMSO).

1984 *Nuclear Power* (CEGB).

1984 Inquiry into Windscale [Black Report] (HMSO).

1985 Report of the House of Lords Select Committee on Nuclear Power in Europe (HMSO).

1985 Report of the House of Commons Select Committee on the Environment: *Radioactive Waste* (HMSO).

1987 Sizewell B Power Station: Statement of Case (CEGB).

1988 Hinkley Point C Power Station: Statement of Case (CEGB).

1988 *Chernobyl: The Government's Reaction* (HMSO).

1988 *The Tolerability of Risk:* Health and Safety Executive (HMSO).

1989 *The Greenhouse Effect: Negotiation Targets* by Michael Grubb (Royal Institute of International Affairs).

1990 House of Commons Energy Committee: Fourth Report: *The Cost of Nuclear Power (HMSO).*

1990 *The Economic Failure of Nuclear Power in Britain* by Alex Hanney (Greenpeace).

*Books*

1964 Margaret Gowing: *Britain and Atomic Energy 1939-45* (Macmillan).

1974 Margaret Gowing: *Independence & Deterrence 1945-52* (Macmillan).

1976 Michael Flood and Robin Grove-White: *Nuclear Prospects* (Friends of the Earth).

1976 World Council of Churches: *Facing up to Nuclear Energy* (Westminster Press, USA).

1977 Dr D Rosling and Dr Hugh Montefiore: *Nuclear Crisis* (Prism Press).

1978 Duncan Burn: *Nuclear Power and the Energy Crisis* (Macmillan).

1979 Robert Jungle: *The Nuclear State* (John Calder).

1980 Jim Garrison: *From Hiroshima to Harrisburg* (SCM Press).

1980 M Stott and P Taylor: *The Nuclear Controversy* (Town and Country Planning Association).

1980 Fred and Geoffrey Hoyle: *Commonsense in Nuclear Energy.*

1980 Roger Williams: *The Nuclear Power Decisions* (Croom Helm).

1981 Sir Alan Cottrell: *How Safe is Nuclear Energy?* (Heinemann).

1981 D J Bennett: *Elements of Nuclear Power*, 2nd ed. (Longman).

1984 J A Camilleri: *The State and Nuclear Power* (Harvester Press).

1986 Judith Cook: *Red Alert* (New English Library).

1986 Kerry Chester: *Nuclear Energy: A Guide to Selected Literature* (BLS).

1986 Walter C Patterson: *Nuclear Power*, 2nd ed. (Penguin). Contains a comprehensive bibliography.